THE ALTERNATIVE SHOPPING GUIDE™

DERBYSHIRE STAFFORDSHIRE CHESHIRE
NORTH SHROPSHIRE

Barbara Cameron

STABLE
PUBLISHING
COMPANY

The Alternative Shopping Guide
Derbyshire, Staffordshire, Cheshire and North Shropshire

Second Edition 2000
The Stable Publishing Company
Woolsthorpe by Belvoir
Grantham, Lincolnshire, NG32 1NT
Tel: 01476 870770
Fax: 01476 870887
www.wctb.co.uk/magazine/alternat.htm

ISBN 1-902634-00-4

British Library Cataloguing in Publication Data
A catalogue record for this book is available from the British Library.

Already published in this series
The Alternative Shopping Guide
Central South & South West England *Second Edition*
ISBN 0-9523761-8-0
The Alternative Shopping Guide
East of England *Third Edition*
ISBN 1-902634-00-4
The Alternative Shopping Guide
Heart of England
ISBN 0-9523761-7-2
The Alternative Shopping Guide
Lancashire & Lake District, North West England
ISBN 0-9523761-4-8
The Alternative Shopping Guide
South East England *Second Edition*
ISBN 0-9523761-3-X

Printed in Great Britain

Contents

ACKNOWLEDGEMENTS

Thank you to all the people who have helped in the production of this book – David for research and the Attractions Section, Judy for her secretarial skills, Henry J Allen (01572 717259) for his photographic work, and many others.

The Stable Publishing Company
Member of:

East of England Tourist Board

Heart of England Tourist Board

North West Tourist Board

southwesttourism
The Regional Tourist Board for the South West of England

Affiliate Member Middle England Fine Foods

Introduction

Winter Sunshine

So often when on holiday, or a day out, we come upon a good farm shop, a speciality shop or fantastic bargains in some totally unexpected location and vow to return. Time passes and we forget or lose the details of the venue. This series of guide books highlights some of the excellent places to be found in North Shropshire, Cheshire, Derbyshire and Staffordshire. Good quality products, reasonable prices, ample parking, beautiful scenery - even those who profess to *hate shopping* will be converted!

We all have to shop, whether for necessities for ourselves or presents for weddings, christenings, Christmas and other occasions. To some it is a chore, to others exciting, but a shopping expedition to some out of the way location is an adventure in itself. Go with an open mind, be prepared for a few surprises, and **take the cool box**! Shropshire, famous for its verdant landscape, sells ice cream in a wide variety of unusual flavours, not far from the picturesque Ellesmere Lakes, and at Sherrifhales, Ted's Farm Shop supplies home-reared beef, pork, lamb and other local goodies. Ironbridge Gorge Museum has some very interesting shops in truly spectacular surroundings. Try visiting the Gorge in autumn or winter, which has the advantage of being quieter, albeit colder, but the landscape is worth admiring whatever the season - shop and explore! Towards Wolverhampton, The Glass Studio at Sunshine Farm engraves glass while you wait, or visit nearby Essington Fruit Farm for fresh fruit and vegetables then return to collect your glass. Both venues are but minutes from major roads but you could well be miles from civilisation at each farm. The Old

Stables Farm Shop and Bakery is a few minutes off the A5 and specialises in home baking - try a rustique loaf with one of their speciality cheeses! One farm in Cheshire sells an incredible array of dried flowers and another has millinery - yes - hats! Who said farm shops only sell food?

Larger complexes can be found near Lichfield at the Curborough Collection - something for everyone and ample free parking, at Brimshage on the Wirral or Lady Heyes Craft and Antique Centre near Frodsham. Nearby Knutsford, with its black and white buildings and narrow streets (but plenty of car parks) has Travelling Light for summer clothing all year round - many at discount prices and ideal for men and women seeking winter sun abroad. Quality clothing at discount prices can also be found on the outskirts of Crewe, Lea Bridge near Matlock, Belper and Alfreton. Household goods ranging from high quality chairs and sofas, to iron bedsteads, handcut crystal to practical pottery, and much, much more can be purchased during a good day out. Many of the places have restaurants or are well placed for good pubs in the most unexpected pockets of countryside.

In winter the black tracery of the leafless trees against a pale blue winter sky has a beauty of its own. In spring, which can be as warm as summer, some of the trees have an almost *yellow* look as the sap rises and the leaf buds burst. The first are usually the willow and the catkins. Celandines, primroses and violets can all be seen after the snowdrops have faded. Gardens and roadside verges are ablaze with daffodils.

We miss much by using only main routes when travelling - *apart from the traffic hold-ups*! Many of the older routes are now much quieter, as was intended, to protect the inhabitants *and* the buildings in small villages and market towns. So go exploring and enjoy your shopping!

Have fun!

Barbara Cameron

How To Use This Book

The area map on pages 18 - 19 is intended to give a general indication of where to find the retail outlets listed in the detailed index on pages 50 - 53. The index will give you the location by number on the area map, and the page number of the entry. To help identify an outlet, all entries are placed in alphabetical order in the index and a local map on the entry page will help you with the last few miles. Opening times do change, so if you are travelling some distance it is advisable to telephone first.

Attractions Of The Region

Strange how words change their meanings for us or drift in or out of fashion. Few use "gay" today in the sense of "jovial" or "happy", and "cool" has certainly added a new meaning. One word that now seems oddly antiquated is "Salop", the old name for the county of Shropshire, part of the region covered by this Alternative Shopping Guide – the north-west Midlands of Derbyshire, Staffordshire, Cheshire and North Shropshire. This is a region only two hours from London, and as different from it as the Cheshire cat is from Cheshire cheese. It's the unexpected variety that makes this one of the most interesting and attractive regions to visit in all England.

Firstly, it's unexpectedly different in its appearance. Here you are out of the lowlands of the south and east England and into the really high ground of the Pennines – 'power walkers' can join the Pennine Way at Edale in Derbyshire, and can continue their 'stroll' north to the Scottish border on the 'top of the world'. The Derbyshire Peak District is really the northern half of that county, and is itself divided into two halves – the White Peak and the Dark Peak. The 'White' is limestone country, with flattish high pastures of small stonewalled fields, cut into by deep steep river valleys – the famous Derbyshire Dales 'gorge-ous'(!) country. The flat-bottomed dales are often wooded and twist through the high ground following the bubbling streams and clear rivers – beautiful in appearance and generally gentle to walk. You can easily become addicted to walking here, for there's a surprise round every bend – a still clear pool or a sudden massive limestone rock in your path, or a secret cave, or the playful disappearance of the river as it slips underground for a mile or two into one of those wonderous limestone cave systems.

The Dark Peak on the other hand has a different mood. This is Millstone Grit country, hard and sombre. Here are the high moors and this is not called the High Peak without reason. Kinder Scout (636ft), Bleaklow Hill (628ft), Featherbed Top (544ft) rise majestically from the bleak moors, and from such heights you can see the shimmering lakes or reservoirs away below you. The most famous of these lakes is perhaps Ladybower – there the famous 'Dambuster' Squadron practised its skills in the Second World War. This is majestic countryside. Try parking in the car park at the top of the Snake Pass (A57 Sheffield-Glossop) for a most amazing view out across the moors one way and far across the Cheshire Plain in the other – but not in winter time!

The Cheshire Plain to the west of the Peak District is something of a misnomer. Certainly it is a rolling lowland in its northern half, with fat sleek cattle ambling in green green pastures round centuries-old half-timbered farm houses. The animals in these fields may well have inspired the Rev. Charles Dodgson ('Lewis Carroll') to include them in his 'Alice's Adventures in Wonderland', for he would have roamed the fields around Daresbury in Cheshire where he was born. The south of the Plain however has some considerable hills – Bickerton Hill in the Peckforton Hills between Chester and Whitchurch will raise a puff or two as you climb it! This area has another magical feature too. This is the land of the 'magpie' house, found all over Cheshire and Shropshire – the black-and-white half timbered buildings, often centuries old, that line the streets of small market towns and villages. Many of these are in Shropshire where the land rolls level across

Cheshire Farmhouse

the great river Severn (never a 'bore'(!)) and rises into the massive Welsh mountains. In fact, if asked for an opinion as to the most attractive town in England, there would be many who would support the suggestion of Shrewsbury in Shropshire. It has so much – a castle, an English Bridge and a Welsh Bridge, magnificent overhung timber and plaster houses that were bright black and white in Elizabethan times, but most excitingly the 'shuts' or winding medieval passages like Gullet Passage or Grope Lane, full of small shops. Ellis Peters created Cadfael, the TV medieval monk private eye, here, and that famous poet, A. E. Housman, the Shropshire Lad, thought Shrewsbury a pretty good place.

Staffordshire has its great literary figures – none more local than Arnold Bennett whose powerful novels were set in the Five Towns that make up Stoke-on-Trent. The north-east of that county shares its geography with the Peak District – Dove Dale and the Manifold Valley are two of the most popular of the 'Derbyshire' Dales, perhaps not so surprising since they are so close to the megablob of the Potteries to the south-west. Not that the Potteries does not have an attraction of its own in the fine bone china you can buy here a great deal cheaper than elsewhere. Staffordshire opens out again in the south into ancient Cannock Chase and fine parkland estates like Shugborough – you will have seen photographs by and of its owner, the famous photographer Lord Patrick Lichfield.

What about going to the sea-side? The sea-side in the Peak District? Well, the next best thing, for this is an area surprisingly full of water attractions. Great lakes abound here, both man-made and natural. Ladybower, Derwent and Carsington are huge stretches of water in Derbyshire, Rudyard in Staffordshire, the Ellesmere Lakes in Shropshire, all offer the pleasures of being near water. And what about a boat trip on a

Ellesmere Lakes

sunny summer afternoon on the vast canal and river system in this region? But Cheshire really does have the sea – for the Wirral Peninsula has some fine beaches on its north and west. Perhaps it's as well not to mention, especially to children, the water attractions of that white-knuckle theme park at Alton Towers on the Derbyshire-Staffordshire border.

What appeals to you most – the scenery, the history, the buildings, the activities, or the oddities of the region you are visiting? Perhaps a taste of all of them – a walk around the walls of Chester, a stroll in Dovedale, an afternoon in the zoo, tea in a lovely 'magpie' inn on the banks of a quiet river. For your convenience, two day-drive routes are suggested that will show you some of the flavour of this most interesting and varied part of England.

ROUTE 1. Peak District

Baslow - Chatsworth - Bakewell - Youlgreave - Arbor Low - Burton - Tideswell - Baslow.

"Horror coldness on the extremities and heat within ... body tinged with a blue dye blotched skin" – symptoms of the bubonic plague that ravaged England from the 13th to the 18th centuries, at its last peak in the Great Plague of 1665. It spread outwards from the ports, especially from London, and in September 1665 reached the hill-top village of Eyam in Derbyshire in a box of tailor's cloth ordered from London. The heroic self-sacrifice of the people of that small innocent community is recorded in the grim lists of names on family tombs in the churchyard. Under the lead of the Rector, William Mompesson, the villagers isolated themselves from all contact with the outside world and prevented the disease spreading out of the village. Elizabeth Hancock lost her husband and six children in a single week. Mary Cooper lost twenty relatives and William Mompesson conducted the burial of his own wife. Take a stroll through the churchyard of this quiet hill-top village when our route takes us that way near the end of our journey.

Baslow in Derbyshire, 12 miles west of the 'crooked spire' town of Chesterfield is the starting point for our drive through the dales and over the moors of the famous Peak District. Only two hours or so from London, this magnificent southern end of the Pennines has a strange remoteness and a delightfully intimate beauty that draws visitors back time and time again. The variety of the scenery is fascinating. At the southern end are deep gorges with grassy paths following the clear waters of busy streams that suddenly disappear into caverns, while in the north, rising over castle-like cliffs or 'edges', are purple open moors and grey bastions of ever higher mountains. The difference of course is due to the nature of the underlying rock, limestone in the southern or 'White' Peak, and the harder grey millstone grit of the northern or 'Dark' Peak. In both are ancient villages tucked around medieval churches, often with their own individual customs practised through hundreds of years. On the lower slopes are great estates carved out in the 16th, 17th and 18th centuries.

Baslow then is our starting point. It is itself a pretty stone village, but as the focal point for entry into the Peak District, it is often busy with traffic, but do look at the ancient three-arched bridge over the Derwent – and as you walk to it, look up at the clock face on St. Anne's Church where instead of figures on the dial, 'VICTORIA 1897' is inscribed.

Take the A619 south and turn off almost immediately onto the B6012 for a breathtaking view of what many believe to be "the finest great house in the finest setting in England", Chatsworth, home of the Duke and Duchess of Devonshire. You could easily spend your day here, taking in the treasures of the vast 18th century house. The 1000 acre park will appeal more even than the house to many. Why? The great Emperor Fountain (named after Tsar Nicholas 1 who stayed here in 1816 – you can see the chestnut tree he planted), the splendid oak tree that Queen Victoria planted in 1832 (the acorns are still collected every autumn to plant for new generations), the Pinus peuce, at 140 ft. the tallest in England, the 'trick' tree, a remarkable willow tree made out of copper that spits out water from every branch – yes, it is the trees and the fountains in the 1000 acre park laid out in 1760 by Capability Brown that appeal most to many who come here.

The variety of the Peak District extends beyond its scenery. Drive on down through Edensor on the Chatsworth Estate (the 6th Duke had the village moved in 1839 to its present site because it obstructed the view!) on to Bakewell, a substantial small town of mellow stone huddled beneath wooded hills, and famous for Bakewell 'tarts' (properly called 'Puddings'), said to originate from a mistake by a cook at the Rutland Arms Hotel in the square whilst making a strawberry tart. Through Bakewell on the A6 South for three miles and you will see the car park and entrance to Haddon Hall, one of the two homes of the Duke of Rutland. Haddon is in total contrast to its great neighbour Chatsworth. Smaller, more romantic, less grand, this medieval manor house has an intimate feel about its Long Gallery and its walled garden – the original slabs still catch your heel as you walk across the uneven courtyard. It seems the perfect setting for the tale of the elopement of pretty Dorothy Vernon with handsome young John Manners one night in 1558 at her sister's wedding party.

Just a mile further along the A6, turn off onto the B5056 and almost immediately off that to Alport and then Youlgreave, an absolutely charming old village set high above one of the most magnificent of the Derbyshire Dales – Lathkill Dale. Walk down (carefully!) into this deep gorge and stroll along the path that runs beside the clear busy little river, full of silent trout and noisy ducks laughing at the walkers. Wooded slopes reach down to the path as you walk further into the dale and great limestone boulders perch above you, reflecting the sunlight. Then the river disappears into its hillside origins, the woods thin out and the tumbled stones and rocks make the upper part of the dale a little more difficult to walk. A very refreshing and satisfying experience.

Lathkill Dale

Cut across westwards now to the A515 and turn north to Buxton. But do not be in too much of a hurry – stop for a quiet moment at the millenia-old 'Stonehenge of the North', Arbor Low Stone Circle, a place of ancient pagan mysteries set high on the moors. Buxton lies in a hollow yet it is one of the highest-sited towns in England, and famous for its spa. As you look down on it, the elegant curve of The Crescent takes your eye – so much like its southern rival in Bath built as it is in classical 18th century style. The Pavilion in 23 acres of gardens is splendid, and the Opera House is the centre for fine concerts with famous artists. This is a lovely town to stroll in.

Out of Buxton now on the A6 eastwards, but for only three miles, then turn north to Blackwell, Miller's Dale and Tideswell and up onto the A623. We are now in the other Peak District, the Dark Peak. Gone now is the light sunny limestone and in its place the more sombre millstone grit. To the north of us are the fiercely steep 'edges' and beyond them the peaty empty moorlands and the really high rounded hills of the High Peak. Tideswell is pleasant for a stroll to see its great gothic church and some interesting buildings behind it, but particularly interesting is the Well-dressing held here early every summer. This is the practice of skilfully decorating the village well with flowers in huge amazing tableaux – probably a thanksgiving for pure water and going back possibly to pre-Christian times. Eyam, Tissington and Youlgreave have some of the best-known well-dressings.

Derbyshire

From Tideswell cross the A623 and head north on the B6049 to Great Hucklow and Grindlow for a view of those great 'edges' – you may well see gliders hovering in the air above you. Incidentally, just a few miles north-west of us lies the opportunity for a very dramatic experience – to enter the underworld of caves at Castleton. Glowing stalacmites and fantastically shaped stalactites reach out of the darkness before you – and buy a piece of that beautifully marked mineral Blue John, found only in this area.

But we are at Great Hucklow. Turn now to the east to Eyam. The tragic impact of the Great Plague when two-thirds of the villagers died in 1665-6 we are already familiar with, but Eyam is a charming village in its own right. Look at that strange clock on the wall of the church near Rev. Mompesson's wife's grave. It tells the time not only in Eyam but across the world by reading the curved line cut into its brass dial.

Finally, we return down the A623 through Calver to our starting point, Baslow. We have had a taste of both White Peak and Dark, noted some beautiful great houses and charming villages, and probably become aware that Derbyshire has somehow preserved a secret history and tradition of its own.

ROUTE 2. High Cheshire

Congleton - Little Moreton Hall and Mow Cop - Rudyard - Gawsworth - Macclesfield - Nether Alderley - Knutsford - Jodrell Bank – Congleton

"Cheshire – land of mountains and moors". But Cheshire is the Cheshire Plain! Far from it. Cheshire is far from being a flat plain. It contains moors and jagged hills, steep wooded valleys and lakes as well as those well-beloved buttercup lowland meadows. Our drive takes us into Cheshire's highlands, and on the way takes in some magnificent country houses and beautiful villages for which this ancient county is famous.

Our journey begins at Congleton, a working market town set where the Cheshire Plain meets the 'highlands'. It is a pleasant town with one or two old timbered inns but far more dormitory housing. Take the A34 south for four miles and stop. You will stop at Scholar Green to see one of the most famous half-timbered manor houses in England, Little Moreton Hall. One of the most attractive and unique characteristics of Cheshire is the 'magpie' house, box-framed 16th century houses with intricate timber patterns and white plaster walls. Little Moreton is the example to see, almost exactly as it was when it was built in 1580 – its great hall is especially attractive, and the moat around it adds a sophisticated necklace to the black-and-white figure of the house. No wonder plays and concerts are often held here – and you can hire an electric narrow boat by the day at nearby Kent Green to add a little 'adventure' to your visit.

Turn east at Kent Green for Mow Cop – you can't miss it, it's a 1,091ft. steep limestone hill with a shaggy turf surface like an Old English

Sheepdog. At the top is a castellated ruined folly – built as a ruin in 1760 by the eccentrically named Randle Wilbraham. What a view from the top over the patchwork fields of the green lowlands!

From the heights descend to the lows – a lake. Cross the A527 at Biddulph, through Biddulph Moor to Rudyard, a pretty village settled beside the great lake below the woods. Yes he was named after the village, for Mr. and Mrs. Kipling became engaged here in 1860. There are most pleasant walks along the shore, and great places to picnic below one of those strange rock formations perched above the lake.

Follow the A523 north (that high hill on your left is The Cloud at 1050ft.). Cross the A54, and then turn off to the left to Gawsworth. This is the more cautious way, but keep your eyes open as you head up the A523. Look especially towards the wild moorland off to your right, for you may be set upon by a wallaby. An Australian wallaby?! Yes – a group of them have survived in the Meerbrook area since an escape from a nearby private estate. In the pleasant village of Gawsworth is another photogenic black-and-white timbered Tudor manor house, set amid lawns and lakes, a lovely place to stop on a warm summer's day. Mary Fitton, the pretty daughter of the house is rumoured to be (among many possibles) the 'Dark Lady of the Sonnets' for she may have caught Shakespeare's eye when she was a maid to Elizabeth 1.

Now it's mill time. Within a few miles of Gawsworth are several most interesting reminders that this area was one of the early centres of silk and cotton production. First, silk. Macclesfield, just a few miles up the A536 was one of the great silk production centres, and in the Silk Museum (fine audio-visual display) and in Paradise Mill (an award-winning centre) are really interesting displays on the silk industry. Paradise Mill has most friendly (and amusing) guides who worked there until it closed in 1981 – and it has a shop. Macclesfield itself has the usual modern shopping centre, but seek out the old core of the town where 'magpie' houses line the hilly streets and cobbled alleyways.

Still with mills but back in time we go as we turn north west on the B5087 to Nether Alderley on the A34, for here there is a much earlier mill, powered not by industrial steam and coal, but by water, just as it was when it was built in the 15th century. It grinds flour now in its pretty setting with a great sloping roof that seems almost to reach the ground, a symbol of an England before the dawn of factories and mass-production.

From Alderley Edge cut west through charmingly named Row o' Trees on to the B5085, and turn west through equally charmingly named Lindow End, Knells Green and Mobberley. Children will be particularly pleased if you visit Hillside Ornamental Fowl centre at Mobberley, for not only are there exotic birds to see like the Abyssinian black duck and the flamingo, but a family of white wallabies and, especially entertaining, a penguin pool. From here it is a pleasant run through the quiet Cheshire countryside to Knutsford.

Magpie Inn

Knutsford encapsulates much of what many believe Cheshire to be – rich green countryside around a prosperous country town full of old timbered houses and quaint magpie inns in narrow streets. To be perfect of course, it has to be the model for a novel, and Knutsford is that too. It is 'Cranford' in Mrs. Gaskell's famous early 19th century novel of that name. An attractive if busy town, one of the reasons for its popularity must be its proximity to Tatton Park, just two miles to the north. This fine Georgian country house built about 1800 is set in over fifty acres of formal gardens – an Edwardian rose garden, a Japanese garden and an Italian garden, glorious in summer. Herds of deer roam the vast park laid out by – no, not Capability Brown, but by another great landscaper, Humphrey Repton. We could toss in a few other great names associated with Tatton if we wished, like Canaletto and Wedgewood – but we will resist.

The last leg of our journey takes in something of the very old and the very modern. Take the A50 south out of Knutsford, but only for two miles or so to the village of Toft. Here a diversion for two miles down and two miles back is suggested – it will be worth your while. Turn onto the B5081 down to what many regard as the most beautiful village in Cheshire, Little Peover, hardly the most appropriate name. Its cobbled lanes, black-and-white ancient houses with their hanging baskets and climbing roses, a glorious timbered 14th century church, all set in quiet watermeadows, will charm you.

Back the two miles to the B5081, turn south for a mile or so and turn southeast on a by-road to Parkgate, Peover Heath and out on to the A535 at Withington Green. You will have seen for miles what the 'very modern' is that were are heading for – the great discs of the radio telescope at Jodrell Bank Science Centre. If our journey had been in the reverse direction, you would never have left Jodrell Bank. Not only is it serious science that will intrigue you, but there is also a fun science centre that neither you nor the children will want to leave. Even the oldest among us will come out wide-eyed with wonder from the vision of the Universe that the Planetarium offers. And finish off with tea and a walk in the arboretum among our own planet's familiar trees.

The quiet run on country by-roads back to Congleton through Withington, Gleadsmoss and Newsbank will calm you down. We have passed through a Cheshire that is so much more than the Cheshire Plain. We have passed through a Cheshire of great variety, of high bleak moors and rolling green fields, quiet rural villages and reminders of industrial power, the very old and the very, very new. One feature that you will probably remember most of all is the timber and plaster 'magpie' house, Cheshire's most famous trademark.

What does this region that is neither north nor south offer us? First, it has immense variety. In a single day you can be high in the bracing Peak District, gently strolling the lanes of rural Cheshire or seeking bargains in the industrial Potteries. Secondly, it is an ancient area with a long long history. Walk the walls of Roman Chester, stand and marvel at Hardwick Hall in Derbyshire, or stroll through a Shropshire village full of overhanging medieval timber and plaster houses that people still have great pride to live in. Finally, the people, by and large are pleasant and friendly – and have their own delicious humour. A Derbyshire farmer was overheard in his local pub one night complaining about water restrictions in a hot summer. "George," he said to his companion, "Did you hear that the Council is going to close three lanes in the swimming pool to save water?"

T. D. Phillips

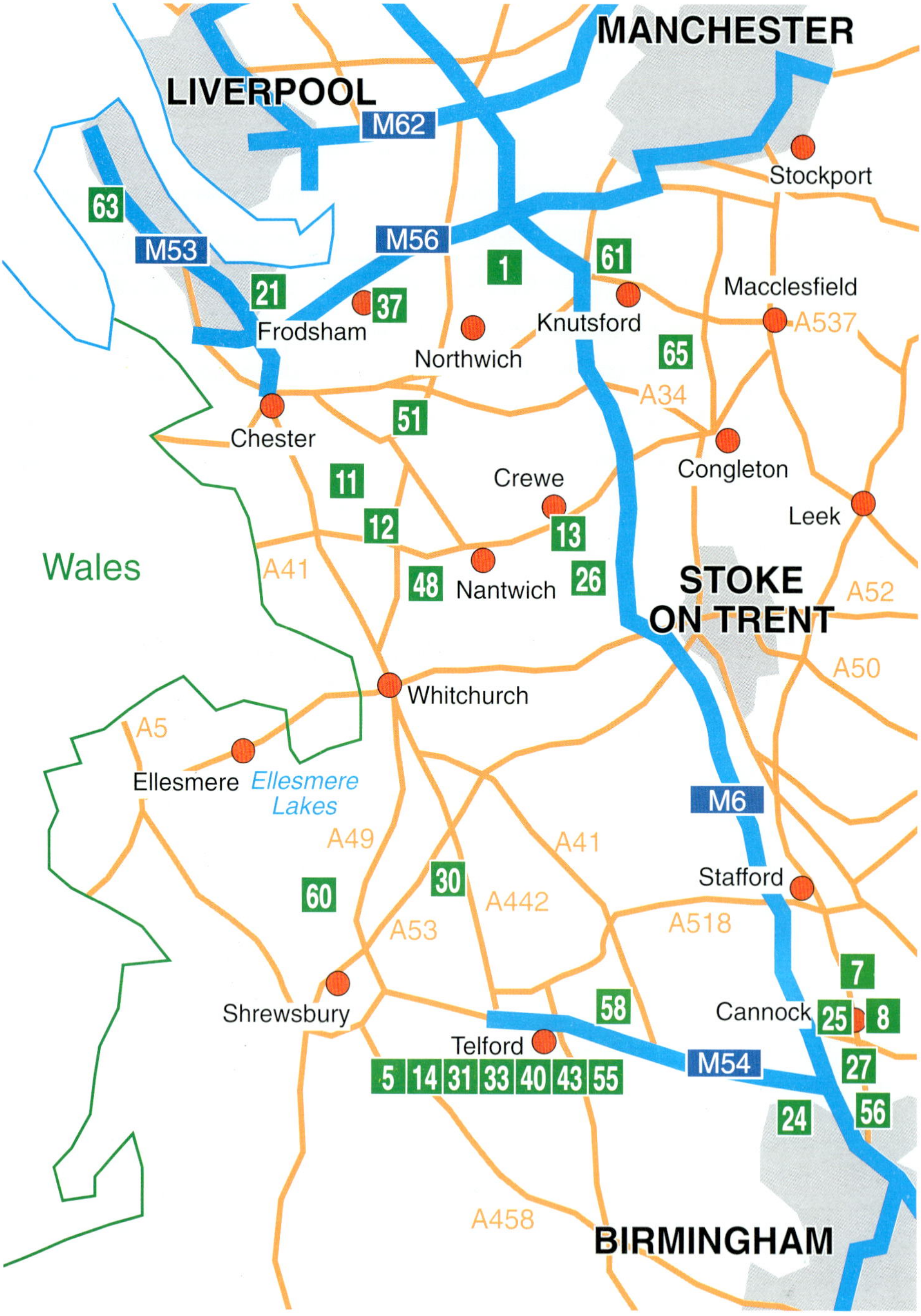
MANCHESTER
LIVERPOOL
M62
Stockport
63
M53
M56
1
61
21
37
Macclesfield
Frodsham
Knutsford
A537
Northwich
65
A34
Chester
51
Congleton
Crewe
11
Leek
12
13
A41
Nantwich
48
26
STOKE ON TRENT
A52
A50
Whitchurch
A5
Ellesmere
Ellesmere Lakes
M6
A49
A41
30
Stafford
60
A442
A518
A53
7
Shrewsbury
Cannock
25
8
58
Telford
M54
27
5
14
31
33
40
43
55
24
56
A458
BIRMINGHAM
Wales

MAP OF THE AREA
SHOWING MAJOR ROUTES

This map is intended for guidance only and you will find more detailed location maps on the appropriate pages. The location numbers refer to the alphabetical index on pages 50 to 53 and not the page numbers.

HAWKSTONE
P A R K
HOTEL, GOLF, FOLLIES AND HISTORIC PARK

Weston-under-Redcastle
Shrewsbury
Shropshire
SY4 5UY
Tel: 01939 200611
Fax: 01939 200311
Email: info@hawkstone.co.uk
www.hawkstone.co.uk

Golf and Leisure shop for quality smart casual clothing for men and women
Gifts, books and more

Open
7 days 8.00am – 5.30pm

Terrace Bar and Restaurant

Open to non-residents

Ample Free Parking

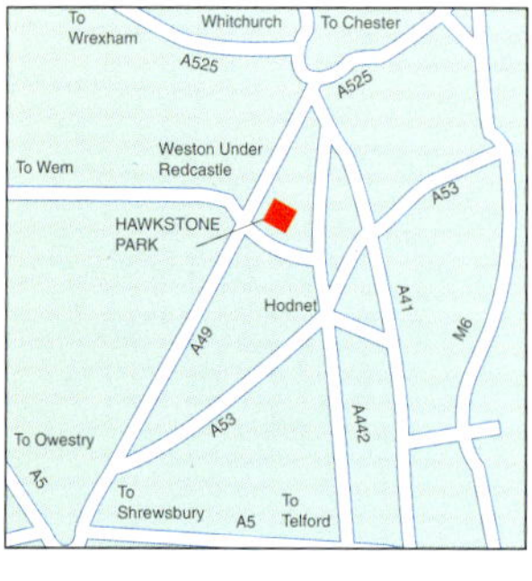

HAWKSTONE PARK

Hawkstone Park, Shropshire's English Heritage designated Grade I landscape, is situated in an idyllic spot, seemingly deep in the countryside, but in reality within easy reach of the M54 and M6 and just off the A49. It has so much to offer golfers, non-golfers, country lovers and dedicated shoppers.

In the **Golf Shop** the range of clothing on offer is carefully chosen for comfort, style and value. Here the ladies will find well-cut trousers and tops and jackets which are ideal for smart casual wear, or more practical for serious walking or golf. Men will be equally impressed, and both will find a good range of knitwear, friendly helpful staff and competitive prices. There is a very good range of gifts, including glass, ornaments, pictures and executive toys and puzzles - not everything appertains to golf. The shop is spacious and well organised and situated in the Golf Centre. The Terrace Bar overlooks the 13th century castle and serves a full range of good value snacks, grills, main meals and alcoholic beverages.

Golfers will know that Sandy Lyle first learned to play on the fairways at Hawkstone Park, non-golfers will appreciate the beautiful landscape and the abundance of walks in the area. You may be tempted to book into the hotel for a few nights and sample some of the other activities which can be arranged. A truly magnificent place to visit.

North Shropshire Specialities

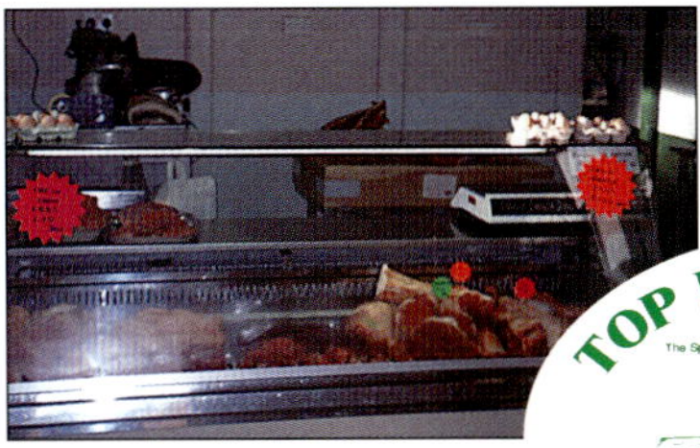

Heart of England Fine Foods was established to promote public awareness of the many fine food and drink products to be found in the counties of Staffordshire, Shropshire, Herefordshire, Worcestershire, Warwickshire and the West Midlands. For a full list of members please telephone during office hours.

The rich pastures of North Shropshire are ideal for livestock and these two independent member businesses are working farms.

Top House Farm Dairy Ice Cream is made on the farm, using only the best natural ingredients to give a smooth, creamy, fresh taste. Vanilla ice cream is still the most popular, but has to compete with Chocolate, Banana, Rum and Raisin, Honey and Nut, Turkish Delight and others. Carton sizes range from small tubs to four litre containers. Delicious fruit sorbets, ideal for those who cannot tolerate dairy products, also come in an exciting range of flavours, including apricot and grapefruit.

Ted's Farm Shop sells traditionally farm-reared beef, pork and lamb. The beef is home-reared from Aberdeen Angus and Hereford cattle fed on grass and additive free home mixed feed. You will also find home dry cured bacon, home-made sausages and burgers, cooked meats, home baked fruit pies, dairy products and free range eggs. Free range turkeys are available to order over the Christmas period, whilst cooked hams can be ordered throughout the year. Well worth searching out, and only a few miles off the A5.

HEART of ENGLAND fine foods

Tel: 01746 785185

Top House Farm
Dairy Ice Cream
The Springs
Cockshutt Ellesmere
Shrops SY12 0JB
Tel: 01939 270237
Email: topice@clara.co.uk

Dairy ice cream & fruit sorbets

Open:
Please telephone for time or name of nearest retail outlet.
Trade enquiries welcome.

Ted's Farm Shop
Hungerhill Farm
Kettlemore Lane
Sherrifhales Shropshire
Tel: 01952 460206
Shop/Fax: 01952 461146

Traditional farm meats, bacon & dairy products

Open:
Thur - Sat 9.00 am - 5.00 pm

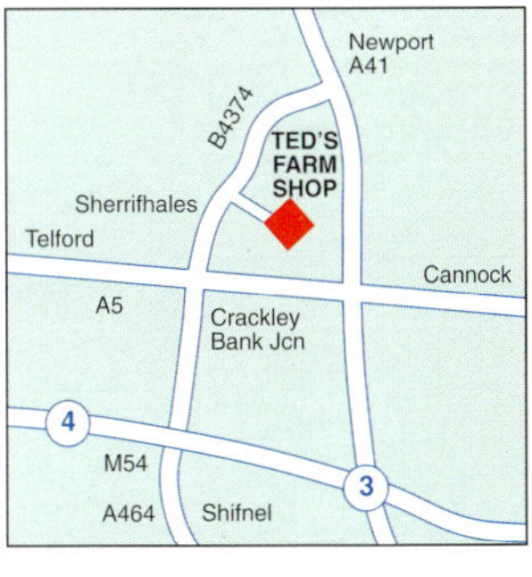

Staffordshire Rural Retailers

Essington Fruit Farm
Bognop Road Essington
Wolverhampton WV11 2BA
Tel: 01902 735724/Fax: 01902 862275

Fresh farm produce
Open: mid June - end Aug
Shop and PYO
9.00am - 9.00pm 7 days
Tearoom 10.00am - 4.00pm (not Mon)
Aug - mid June
Shop 9.00am - 5.00pm Tues - Sun
(closes 2.00pm Sun, Christmas - Easter)
Tearoom 11.00am - 3.00pm
Sat and Sun only

The Glass Studio and Sunshine Farm Plants
Sunshine Farm
Hilton Lane Essington
Wolverhampton WV11 2AU
Tel: 01922 416948

Cut crystal & engraved glass. Plants
Open: Tues - Sun 9.00am - 5.00pm

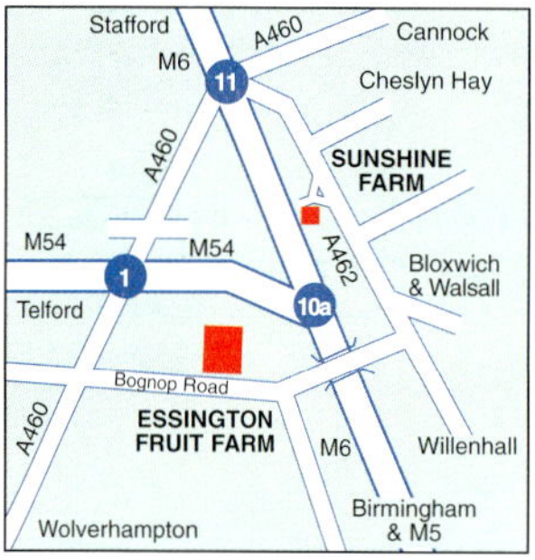

The Old Stables Farm Shop
Packington Moor Farm
Packington Lichfield WS14 9QA
Tel: 01543 481223

Fruit & vegetables, cheeses, bacon & specialities. PYO soft fruits. Catering service.
Open: Shop
Tues - Sat 8.00am - 6.00pm
Winter: Closed Sun and Mon
Summer: Open Sunday 9.00am - 5.00pm. Closed Mon.
PYO in season 10.00am - 8.00pm
7 days

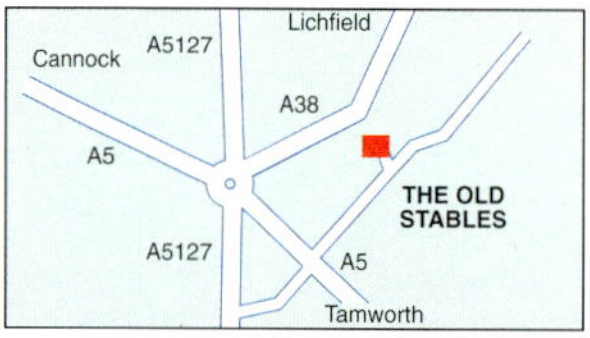

Staffordshire Rural Retailers

A stones throw from the busy M6, Staffordshire has some lovely unspoilt countryside where a diverse selection of quality products can be found.

Essington Fruit Farm specialises in a wide range of Pick Your Own fruit and vegetables. The less energetic will always find them ready-picked in the spacious shop, alongside home baked pies, cakes and bread plus preserves and pickles. The Country Kitchen Tearoom and Restaurant is always open at weekends and also weekdays in high summer, whilst outside the plant nursery offers quality bedding plants, perennials and shrubs at very competitive prices - and don't forget the Christmas trees!

At **The Glass Studio**, set behind mature woodland, Catherine Downes has been engraving glass for 27 years. She will personalise items for any occasion from the sparkling collection of glassware on show. Inscriptions are sometimes engraved while-you-wait but sand-blasting will take a little longer. Alongside, Carl Downes runs **Sunshine Farm Plants** using redundant glass houses from his farming days for vegetables, perennials, alpines, pansies, shrubs, climbers and bedding plants.

The Old Stables Farm Shop and Bakery is a true country food store, stocking fresh fruit and vegetables and home grown potatoes as well as a huge range from the bakery including speciality breads. Other products include farmhouse cheeses, bacon, pâtés, pickles and preserves, cordials, ice cream and Christmas specialities. Pick Your Own soft fruits are available in early summer and refreshments can be served in the Courtyard. A catering service can be provided in your home or office for any occasion.

IRONBRIDGE GORGE MUSEUMS

The beautiful Ironbridge Gorge, spanned by the world's first Iron Bridge, is steeped in history and enhanced by nature. This unique area was the birthplace of the Industrial Revolution and the Ironbridge Gorge Museums interpret the valley's history and provide an excellent value 'Passport' ticket giving entry to most Museums.

Discover Coalport China, Coalbrookdale iron and Jackfield's decorative tiles. Take time to visit the "Time Capsule" at **Broseley Clay Tobacco Pipe Works**, with a small shop next door specialising in tobacco pipes and accessories, or don your hard hat for a trip down the Tar Tunnel. Do not miss the opportunity to talk with "Victorian Townsfolk" at Blists Hill, where specialist products and craftsmen-made items can be found within the Museum.

Visit the **Shop in the Square** housed in the old grocer's shop adjacent to the Iron Bridge. This excellent gift shop stocks an ever changing variety of quality gifts in a wide price range. Stroll beside the River Severn to the **Museum of the Gorge** and onto the **Merrythought Teddy Bear Shop**.

Coalport China Museum Shop stocks wide ranges of Coalport and Wedgwood giftware. Over the river is **Jackfield Tile Museum Shop** where the Museum's collections are the inspiration for tiles produced on site and sold in this unique factory shop, with highly imaginative ideas for home decoration and gifts.

Museum-made cast-iron door porters can be found at **Blists Hill Victorian Town** and **Museum of Iron Shops**, along with cards, books and delicious confectionery & preserves.

Ironbridge
VALLEY OF INVENTION

Ironbridge Gorge
Telford
Shropshire TF8 7AW
Tel: 01952 433522
01952 432166
E-mail:
info@ironbridge.org.uk
Internet:
www.ironbridge.org.uk

Crafts, tiles, gifts, teddybears, china, books & much more

Shops opening hours
7 days 10.00am – 5.00pm
Winter openings may vary - please check.
Broseley open April - Nov
1.00pm - 5.00pm

FREE ENTRY
to shops

Museums
Same opening as for shops shown above

'Passport' ticket gives entry to all major museum sites

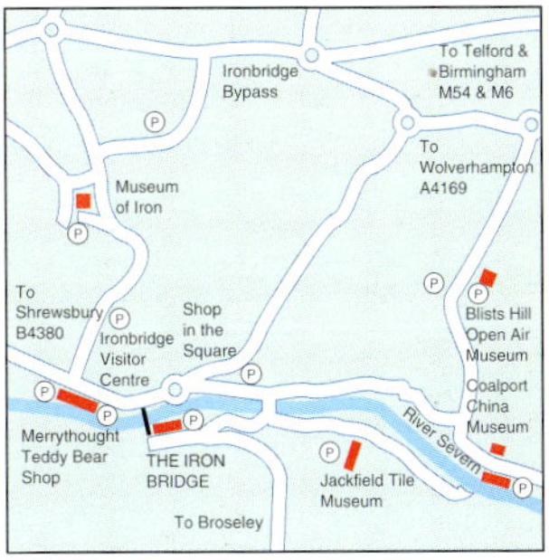

Voirrey Embroidery

The Voirrey Embroidery Centre
Brimstage Hall
Brimstage Wirral Cheshire
CH63 6JA
Tel: 0151 342 3514
Fax: 0151 342 5161

Everything for embroidery, tapestry and needlework
Screens, footstools
Specialist books
Framing and making up service

Exhibitions
(free admission)
Courses

Open
7 days
Mon – Sat
10.00am – 5.00pm
(to 8 pm on the first Thursday of the month)
Sundays 1.00 – 5.00pm

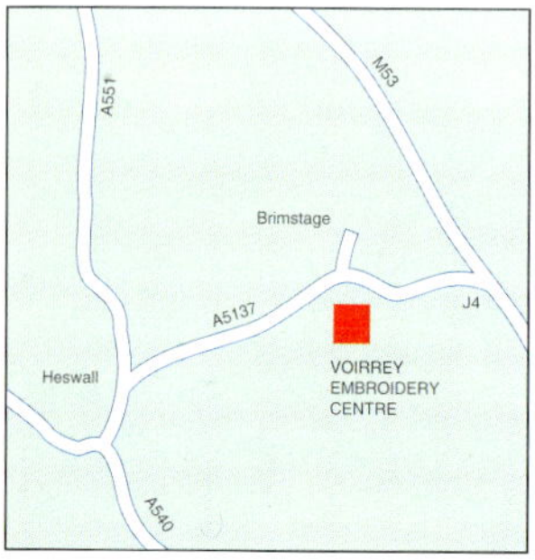

The Voirrey Embroidery Centre

'The well known Voirrey Embroidery Centre was founded in 1983 in a small crypt within Brimstage Hall, but four years later had outgrown the space and moved into its present home, which was extended three years later. It now occupies one side of the Brimstage Hall Courtyard, a rectangle of old farm buildings behind the 12th century manor house. The building had been the original wainhouse, stables and grain mill and the old beams have been preserved, forming a fitting setting for a craft older than the buildings.

Here you can buy everything for all types of needlecraft - from needles to canvas, silks, wools, frames, mounts, wadding, quilting fabrics and tapestry kits. The array of kits selected from the world's best suppliers includes counted cross-stitch and traditional and modern surface embroidery. There is a growing portfolio of exclusive Voirrey kits - no wonder she was voted Merseyside Business Woman of the Year in 1993.

The shop is extremely well fitted and organised into departments thus making it easier to choose your purchases. The staff are well qualified to advise you, if required, whether you are a beginner or an experienced needleworker. A wide range of specialist books is stocked - watch for the book launches with the author in attendance and visit the exhibitions on the first floor, which change monthly, some of international importance. Enquire about specialist courses.

RAVENS OAK DAIRY

Ravens Oak Dairy at Burland Farm is easily found on the A534 Nantwich to Wrexham road. The Allwood family have lived and farmed here for eight generations. Michael and Sandra Allwood, the present occupants, have returned to the family tradition of cheesemaking. Fine hand-made soft cheeses are produced with milk from their own dairy herd. The farm will be registered organic in July 2000 after a two year conversion period.

Goat and buffalo cheeses are also made in the dairy, and won Gold, Silver and Bronze awards for the best new or experimental cheeses at the British Cheese Awards 1999. All cheeses will be available from the Dairy Shop which is scheduled to open late 1999. It is also intended to stock a wide range of organic products and vegetables as well as environmentally friendly cleaning materials. The aim is to enable customers to do a "one-stop" organic shop or to supplement other shopping. Freshness and quality are paramount with goods and produce sourced as locally as possible, for example bread from Snapes Bakery in Woore.

Over the next eighteen months there are plans to move the shop from its temporary quarters to a refurbished, listed Victorian farm building, which will incorporate a tea room serving fresh organic food. A treat to look forward to. Further plans include having rare breed pigs and chickens to watch and growing a year-round variety of vegetables and soft fruit to supply the shop and tea-room.

Ravens Oak Dairy is a member of North West Fine Foods, an organisation formed to promote the best of locally produced food and drink.

Ravens
Oak
Dairy

Burland
Nantwich
Cheshire
CW5 8ND
Tel: 01270 524624
Fax: 01270 524724

Hand-made soft cheeses
Goat and buffalo cheeses
Organic products

Tea Room
scheduled for end 2000.
B&B available.

Open
Wed - Sun
9.00am - 6.00pm
(other times
please telephone)

On site parking

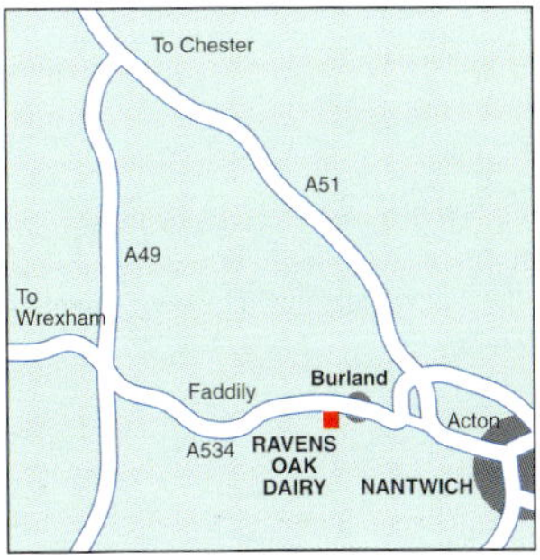

Cheshire Workshops
THE CANDLE MAKERS

Cheshire Workshops
The Candle Makers
Burwardsley
Nr Tattenhall
Cheshire CH3 9PF
Tel: 01829 770401
Candles, gifts, pottery, glass, china, leatherwork & crafts
Childrens play area
Restaurant
Open 7 days all year
10.00am – 5.00pm
Closed Christmas Eve & Christmas Day

Cheshire Ice Cream Farm
Drumlan Hall Farm
Newton Lane Tattenhall
Cheshire
Tel: 01829 770995
Dairy ice cream, sorbets, cheese & preserves
Restaurant
Open 7 days
April - Oct 10.00am -5.30pm
Nov-March 10.30am-5.00pm
Closed for 2 weeks late Jan early Feb

Free Parking at both sites

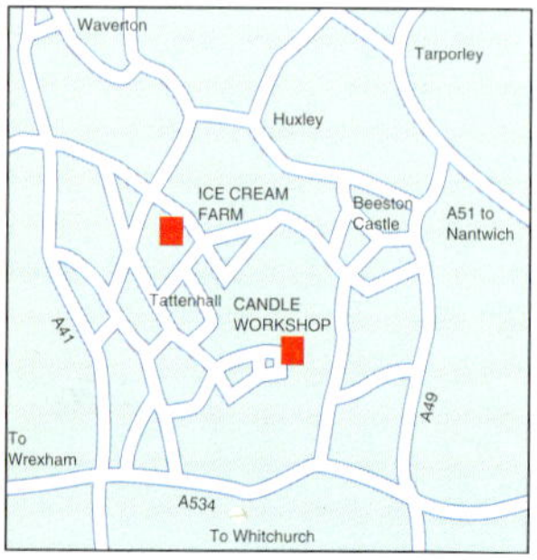

Cheshire Workshops & Cheshire Ice Cream Farm

Rising steeply from the Cheshire Plain is a sandstone ridge from the top of which the view is incredible. Here you will find **Cheshire Workshops**. The old stone buildings house the candle-making factory where you can watch craftspeople sculpture beautifully designed and colourful candles before making purchases. This Aladdin's Cave is full of interesting and unusual gifts, many handcrafted using techniques from a bygone age, including pyrography, leatherwork and hand made pottery and china. Glass sculptures are made on site and open to view. The birds and flowers are beautifully delicate and colourful, and, like everything else here, very reasonably priced. Children can "have a go" at making candles, badges and pottery, or amuse themselves outside in the play area, or watching the goats on goat mountain. You can all relax in **Chandlers Restaurant** with coffee and delicious home made scones, a snack, or full à la carte menu - again at very reasonable prices. This room is also available for functions.

Nearby, and belonging to the same family, is **Cheshire Ice Cream Farm**, offering a real taste of Cheshire, an opportunity to see a dairy farm at work, an insight into how ice cream is made and a mouth-watering chance to sample, (*free of charge*), some of the thirty different flavours of ice cream or sorbets before purchasing. Take the coolbox and finish your visit in **Caroline's Pantry** with a light lunch or afternoon tea.

GET AHEAD HATS

Hats are experiencing a wonderful revival and it is just *not done* to be hatless at a wedding, the races, graduation ceremonies and various other occasions. **Get Ahead Hats** showrooms are all franchised from the parent company in Yorkshire and run by farmers' wives. They all offer *friendly service in a country setting*, and School Farm is no exception.

Caroline Lowe has a well-fitted showroom with an extensive range of hats for all occasions. Simple classic elegance, bold eye-catching styles, light concoctions in fabulous colours, are all there to be tried. If you require something extra special to match an outfit a hat can be individually hand made from fabrics to match your outfit and trimmed to match your accessories. All the hats are very "wearable" and as fit is important so that you feel comfortable the size can be adjusted - nothing worse than having to hold your hat every time you lower your head!

Take your outfit to try on with the hats - a fitting room is available, and take your time! Ask for advice; take a friend with you and be prepared to be transformed. Hats have a way of making us feel well-groomed and elegant whatever our age.

All hats are available to hire or to buy and customers return time and time again.

School Farm
Hassall Nr Sandbach
Cheshire CW11 4SA
Tel/Fax: 01270 760169

Hats for hire and sale for all occasions

Open
9.00am – 6.00pm
6 days
but please telephone first.
Evening appointments available.

Ample parking on site

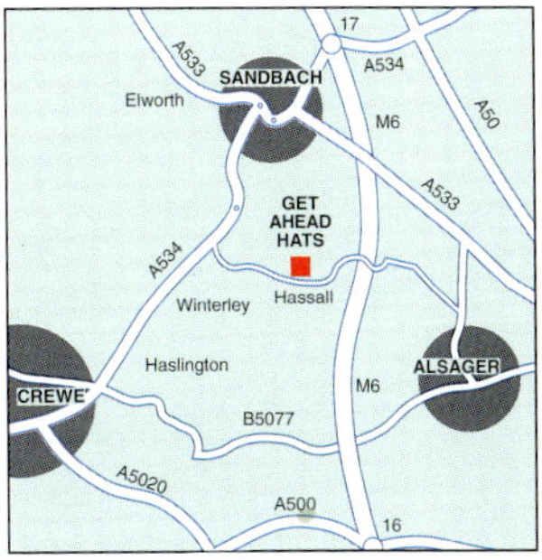

WELLTROUGH DRIED FLOWERS

DRIED FLOWERS, BASKETS AND ARRANGEMENTS

Welltrough Hall Farm
Lower Withington
Nr Macclesfield
Cheshire
SK11 9EF
Tel: 01477 571616

Dried flowers (bunches and arrangements)
silk flowers and florists accessories
Demonstrations and courses

Open
Mon-Fri 9-5
Sat and Sun 10-5
closed 3 days at Christmas and New Year
telephone for details

Ample FREE parking

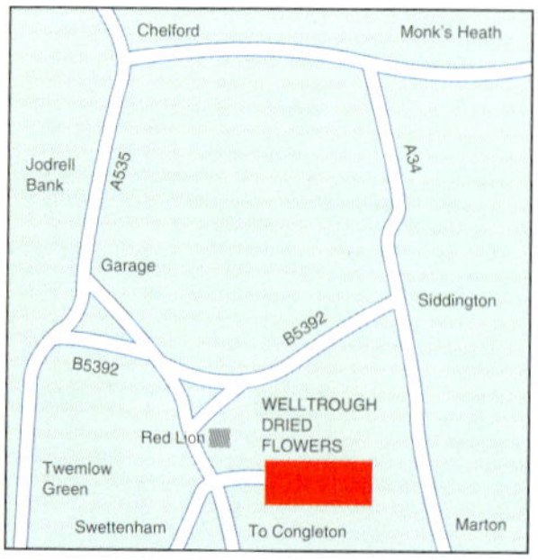

WELLTROUGH DRIED FLOWERS

In the heart of Cheshire farming country, and close by Jodrell Bank Radio Telescope is Welltrough Hall Farm - a typical half-timbered black and white building, set on a bank surrounded by lush pastures. Converted farm buildings are home to a huge selection of silk and dried flowers and floral arrangements at prices to suit all pockets.

This business has expanded rapidly over the last few years and now has nine showrooms, each specialising in particular types or colours of flowers and arrangements to make it easier for you to make a choice. You are free to browse and staff are on hand to give advice if required. Specific arrangements can be commissioned although with so much to choose from you are more likely to be spoilt for choice. Perhaps you prefer to make your own arrangements? Everything is available for this, including courses and workshops if you need help.

Barry Grey, the nationally renowned demonstrator illustrates his skills for groups of up to 100 people. The fee for this covers an hour's demonstration, light refreshments and 10% discount on purchases made that day.

A new addition is a permanent Christmas Room that out of season offers big discounts so you can stock up early! The family can wander round the animal area which houses cows and calves, and other animals. Outside is a pond with rare breeds of ducks.

Travelling Light

Travelling Light is the only company in the U.K. which specialises in hot weather clothing all year round. So if you are planning a winter sun holiday you can find a light, cool, co-ordinating range of clothing for men and women in the depths of a British winter, when all other shops are stocking overcoats. The firm was started in 1987 by Freddy and Suzie Markham, and nearly all the clothing is designed and made in their Cumbrian factory, using top quality fabrics from around the world. Travel, trekking, safari, cruise and beach clothing is well made from the most suitable materials at value-for-money prices.

There is a comprehensive range of useful, stylish travel accessories, such as belts and bags, hats, shoes and boots. The mail order catalogue is full of useful practical items which make wonderful gifts and a full range of clothing. However, there are now seven shops throughout the country. Within easy reach of the M6, in the historic town of Knutsford, with its narrow streets, old buildings and good eating places, **Travelling Light** has a double shop. Here you will find a permanent Bargain Section for the end of lines at big discounts, spacious changing rooms and a comfortable sitting room, where your companion can read the papers and enjoy tea or coffee whilst you make your selection. Alteration to length is free of charge and there is a Made to Measure service for non-standard sizes.

TRAVELLING LIGHT

5 & 7 Minshull Street
Knutsford
Cheshire WA16 6HG
Tel: 01565 621075

Hot weather clothing for men and women all year round plus a range of high quality travel accessories

Open:
Mon - Sat 10.00 am - 5.00 pm
(closed Sundays and Bank Holidays)

Mail Order telephone:
01931 714488

Nearby car parking

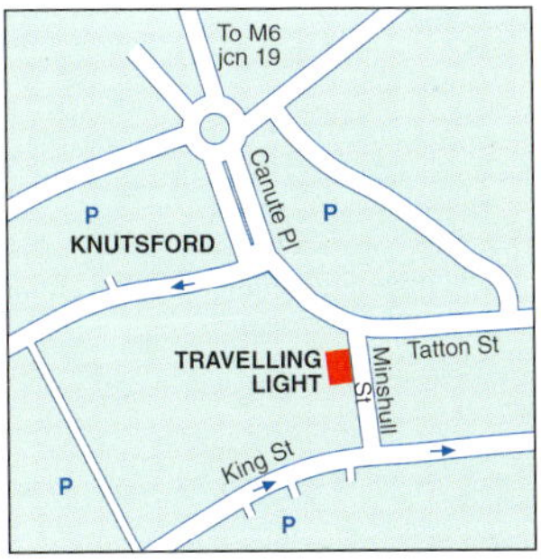

Rose Farm Shop

Rose Farm
Utkinton Tarporley
Cheshire CW6 0LP
Tel: 01829 732978

Farm fresh produce, locally produced meats, poultry, cheeses, quiches, breads and cakes, and more

Off-licence and Post Office

Open
Mon - Fri
8.00am – 6.00pm
Sat
8.00am - 5.00pm
Sun & Bank Holidays
9.00am - 1.00pm

Large free car park

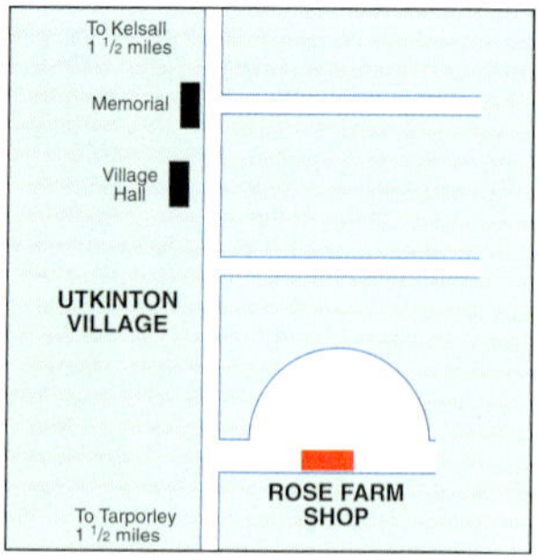

Rose Farm owned by the Johnson family was known as "The Steps" at the turn of the century, and became a Post Office around 1904, when another shop opened selling general groceries and later, fresh vegetables. Bread was delivered from Tarporley and meat came from the slaughterhouse. Utkinton community was virtually self-sufficient. Over the years the general store changed hands and a new building became The Village Stores and Post Office - this closed in 1996. John Johnson, now selling home-produced meat from the farm, recognised the opportunity to merge both businesses. And so the Post Office returned to **Rose Farm**.

This purpose built friendly shop, opened in 1997, is so much more than a *farm shop*. The beef comes from traditional British cattle, raised on pasture free from artificial fertilisers and chemicals. Pigs are also allowed to roam free, and lamb and poultry is obtained locally. All meat traceable to source, and professionally prepared by traditional butchers. The shop prides itself on its selection of British Farmhouse cheeses, locally made pies, quiches, cakes and bread. Many of the fruits and vegetables are local, the more exotic from elsewhere. A good choice of wines and spirits is available to complete a good meal; add general groceries at competitive prices and all your shopping is done.

Plants and garden sundries complete the stock, whilst cattle look over the fence.

CHESTER BARRIE

Chester Barrie has been making tailored garments for over 60 years for the discerning customer. Using only the finest cloths, the skilled tailors handcraft styles in the best English tradition. Almost half the total production is made for export to Europe, USA and Japan - in fact world wide, and the company has its own shop in Savile Row, London.

The factory shop in Crewe gives you the opportunity to make purchases at discounted prices. Adjustments to fit can be carried out if necessary and the helpful and friendly staff will be pleased to assist. Styles range from modern and contemporary for the younger man to traditional styling for the more conservative. There is also a Bespoke Tailoring service, whereby customers can select their own cloth and style of garment and collect their perfectly fitting Chester Barrie garment eight weeks later, following an interim fitting. An office or home visit can be arranged.

Ladies clothes are equally beautifully tailored - classic, understated and subtle. The type of clothes that last and last and can be worn for all sorts of occasions - the office, the boardroom, the formal function or more casually at weekend country events. A good selection of shirts, blouses, trousers and skirts is always available, plus shoes and accessories.

Well worth a visit if you appreciate quality, service and fine styling. Sometimes samples are available at even more tempting prices!

Chester Barrie
SAVILE ROW

Weston Road
Crewe
Cheshire
CW1 6BA
Tel: 01270 508900

Handcrafted tailored suits for ladies and gentlemen
Shirts, blouses, trousers, skirts, topcoats and accessories
Discount prices

Open
Mon - Fri
10.00am - 4.30pm
Sat
9.00am - 3.30pm

Own free car park

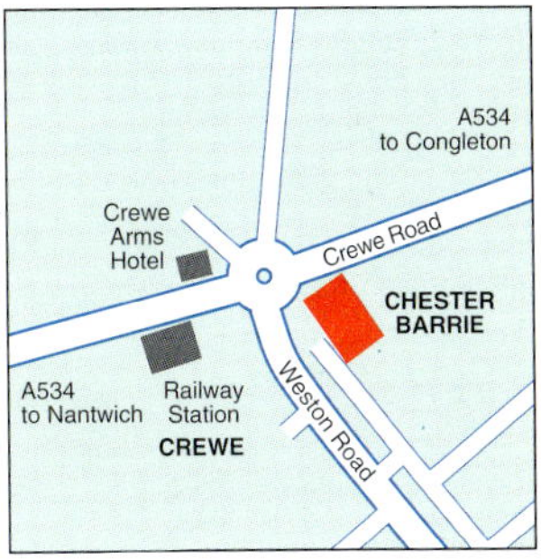

Lady Heyes Craft &
Antique Restoration Centre
Kingsley Road
Frodsham
Cheshire WA6 6SU
Tel: 01928 787919

Collection of individual units specialising in crafts and antiques

Tearooms

Open
7 days
Mon - Sat 10.00am - 5.00pm
Sun 11.00am - 5.00pm

Ample free parking

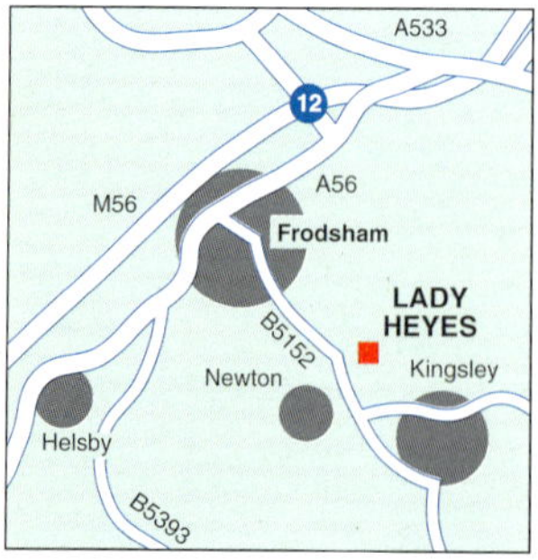

Lady Heyes Craft & Antique Restoration Centre

Lady Heyes Farm has been on this site for several hundred years. It is believed that back in the 1800s it was used as a watering hole for the local gentry. Whilst the gentlemen were at the local tavern, the ladies, after their day of hunting, would stop at Lady Heyes Watering Hole to water their horses. No longer a working farm, the buildings are now a *happy hunting ground* for a wide selection of crafts, gifts and antiques.

Lady Heyes Craft and Antique Restoration Centre was established in September 1999 and whatever your tastes or budget you are bound to find something to your liking. There is wood-turning, painted furniture, hand made cabinets, pine furniture and antiques for every room in the house, whether it be a country cottage or a modern town house. Textiles include soft furnishings, lace making, cross-stitch kits and antique linens, whilst giftware includes painted glass, papier-mâché sculptures, books, crystals, candles, paper crafts, hand made ornaments and greetings cards. There is a good display of work by local artists and more units are being opened.

The tearooms offer light lunches and snacks in comfortable surroundings, whilst you contemplate your purchases. The hand made chocolates are worth travelling miles for - an ideal treat for yourself!

ARLEY HALL & GARDENS

This beautiful and historic house, set in magnificent gardens and parkland has been a private family home for five hundred years. The first **Arley Hall** was built about 1469 on the present site and remained with few alterations for some three hundred years. It was encased in new walls of brick and stucco by Sir Peter Warburton, who was also Chairman of the management committee of Cheshire gentlemen who completely rebuilt and modernised the Weaver Navigation Works in the 1750s and 1760s. A great and energetic agricultural improver, Sir Peter built several model farms on the estate, built the first of the existing walled gardens and laid out new gardens to the east of the house.

The Gardens are a riot of colour, with herbaceous borders, sculptured yew hedges, terraces, formal gardens within mellow brick walls, kitchen gardens and cottage gardens. The woodland garden has been developed gradually over the last thirty years and extensions are constantly evolving.

The Gift Shop has a good range of carefully selected gifts and a wide variety of books - many on plants as you would expect. Unique video and audio cassettes will make a wonderful reminder of your visit.

The Restaurant is licensed and offers a relaxed atmosphere for coffee or a full meal, inside or out dependent on the weather.

Arley Hall & Gardens
Near Northwich
Cheshire CW9 6NA
Tel: 01565 777353
or 777284
Fax: 01565 777465
Email:
Arley@Info-Quest.com

Gardens, grounds, gift shop and licensed restaurant

Open
9 April - 1 Oct
Tues to Sun and
Bank Holidays
11.00am - 5.00pm

Hall Open
Sundays and one weekday.
Please telephone.
(Admission charge).

Special Events
Antique Fairs
Craft Fairs
Art Exhibitions
Christmas Shopping Events
Concerts
Corporate Functions
(Please telephone for details)

Ample parking

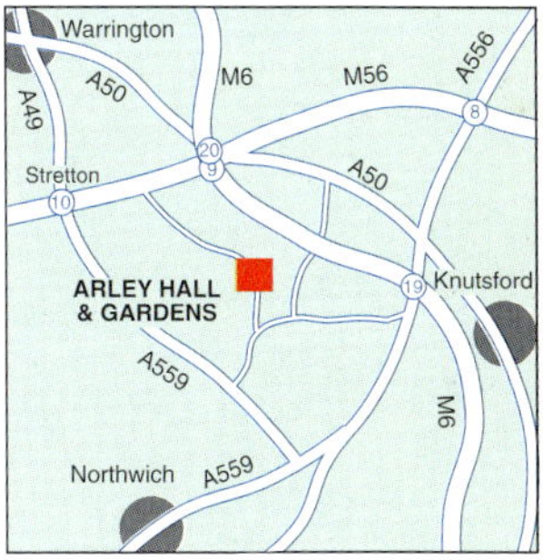

THE OLD HARTINGTON CHEESE SHOP

Hartington
Derbyshire SK17 0AH
Tel: 01298 84496
www.hartingtoncheese.com

British cheeses

Open
7 days
9.00am - 4.30pm

Free car parking is available in the village centre and around the village pond

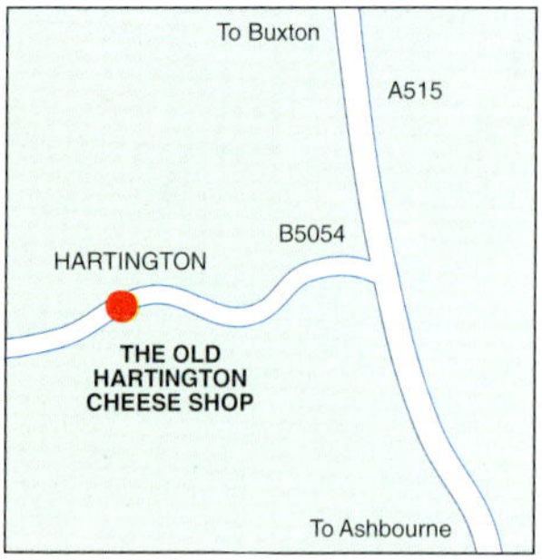

The Old Hartington Cheese Shop is located right in the heart of the tiny Derbyshire village of Hartington and is run by the Dairy Crest Hartington Creamery.

Established by the Duke of Devonshire in 1870, generations of Hartington families have, through the years, worked at both the creamery and the shop which fronts it. Today, some of the finest blue cheeses in Britain are produced here and awards are won on a regular basis.

The Shop is the "shop window" for cheeses made at the Creamery as well as other Dairy Crest cheeses. It also offers over 60 excellent cheeses from around Britain. The range available includes traditional Blue and White Stilton, favourites such as Cathedral City Cheddar and Red Leicester, local Peak District cheeses like Dovedale and Buxton Blue and special delicacies such as Swaledale.

The Old Hartington Cheese Shop also has its very own website through which the full history of the creamery and shop can be accessed. A description of every cheese at the shop is also available along with advice on cheese combinations, how to store cheese and which wines should accompany different flavours. Fascinating for anyone who enjoys good cheese! Cheese selections can be purchased through a secure credit card payment system and delivered anywhere in the UK if you are unable to visit this delightful village yourself.

CARSINGTON WATER

Courtesy: Severn Trent Water

Carsington Water is Britain's newest reservoir, blending naturally into the hilly landscape between Wirksworth and Ashbourne in Derbyshire. The Visitor Centre has an award-winning exhibition showing the reliability and value of a clean water supply, which is as fascinating as it is educational. The **Severn Trent Water Shop** has an abundance of good quality, reasonably priced gifts including glass, stationery, greetings cards, souvenir items, preserves, and Crabtree and Evelyn toiletries.

Acorn Country Gifts has a wonderful selection of country clothing for all ages, china, toys of all types from soft toys to puzzles, jewellery and some very unusual reasonably prices gifts for the home.

The Embroidery Box stocks everything required for needlecraft - canvas and wool, silks, needles, frames and fabrics to complicated tapestry kits. Jan Staniforth is always willing to offer help and advice.

Waterside offers a fascinating choice of gifts, antiques, pot pourri decorative items and linens - just that little bit different and competitively priced. The fifth shop in this complex is **Kath Thorpe Ceramics and Country Bookstore** where Kath's highly individual hand made ceramics are for sale alongside other distinctive studio pottery from Britain and overseas. Part of this shop is devoted to a wide selection of books, many at bargain prices.

There is literally something for everyone here and your visit can be completed with a brisk walk by the water whatever the time of year or simply visit the restaurant and admire the view.

Carsington Water

Carsington Water Ashbourne
Derbyshire DE6 1ST

Visitor Centre and Severn Trent Water Shop
Tel: 01629 540 696
gifts, cards, children's items, glass, pottery, pictures

Acorn County Gifts
Tel: 01629 540 692
toys, china, jewellery, country clothing

The Embroidery Box
Tel: 01629 540 668
everything for needlecraft

Waterside
Tel: 01629 540 274
gifts and antiques

Kath Thorpe Ceramics and Country Bookstore
Tel: 01629 540 240
studio pottery and books

Open
All year (except Xmas Day) from 10.00 am - (closing times vary) FREE admission (small parking charge)

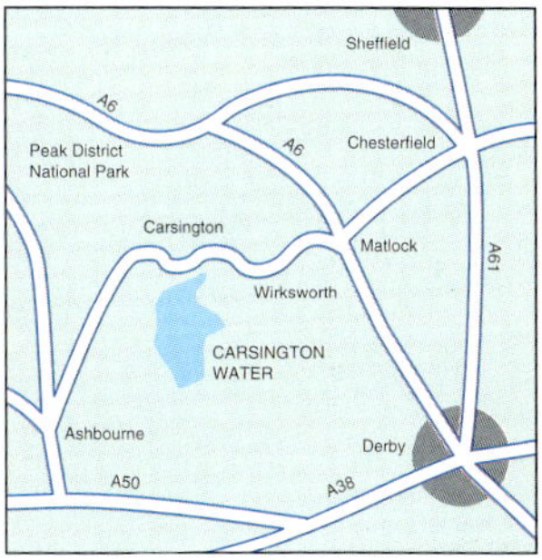

MASSON

EST 1783

Shopping Village and
Historic Mills
Matlock Bath
Derbyshire
Tel: 01629 760208

Shopping Village
Open all year
Mon - Fri 9.30am - 5.30pm
Sat 9.30am - 6.00pm
Sun 11.00am - 5.00pm

Free admission

Knitwear, leisurewear, outerwear, golf equipment & clothing, textiles, fabrics Pottery, china, gifts, traditional perfumes, food, nuts & confectionery Restaurant & Tea Room

Working Textile Museum
(admission charge)
Mon - Sat 10.00am - 4.00pm
Sun 11.00am - 4.00pm

Large free car park

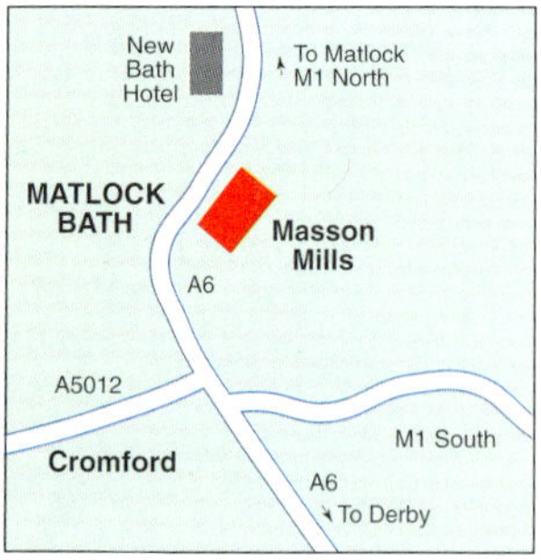

MASSON MILLS

Masson Mills are internationally famous as the show piece mills of Sir Richard Arkwright, the "Father of the Factory System", two centuries ago. **The Working Textile Museum** allows you to see at first hand what life was like in a cotton mill - Arkwright's ghost is said to wander the old rooms - no doubt comparing the past and present textiles!

The Shopping Village, on four floors of this Grade II listed building also specialises in textiles, with a good selection of well-known names displaying their goods. **The Edinburgh Woollen Mill** offers quality knitwear, leisurewear and outerwear, whilst **The Golf Company** has a range of top class golf clothing and equipment. Household textiles are supplied by **Ponden Mill** and include bedding, towels, curtaining, tableware and cushions - all at affordable prices to suit all budgets. If it is presents you are looking for consider **Woods of Windsor** for traditional perfumes and soaps, or **Poole Pottery** for china and gifts. **Julian Graves** has a huge range of dried fruit, nuts, confectionery and speciality foods and preserves - once tempted by these you'll be back again and again!

The Derwent Restaurant is licensed, has a full menu and overlooks the river, or enjoy a satisfying snack or cream tea in **The Arkwright Tea Room** after a stroll along the banks of the River Derwent which provided a plentiful power supply to the old mills.

JOHN SMEDLEY LIMITED

John Smedley Ltd has been producing fine gauge luxury knitwear for over 200 years at its mill in a picturesque valley two miles from the main A6 at Cromford. Lea Mills was built by Peter Nightingale, great-uncle of Florence Nightingale and she often visited the works to help the employees. Associated with Peter Nightingale was Thomas Smedley, whose family still run the business. Skills have been passed down through generations of workers and the name **John Smedley** is synonymous with fine gauge knitted products world wide.

The shop, on the opposite side of a large car park, is well fitted and well-stocked. There is always a wide choice of end of ranges or slight seconds from the company's extensive collection of men's and ladies' luxury knitwear produced from the finest natural raw materials. Sea Island cotton is a fine, smooth, soft cotton which makes superb polo shirts in a wide range of colours and sizes. Extra fine Merino wool retains its lustre, resilience and shape after long wear and is exclusively farmed for the company in New Zealand. Design samples, discontinued styles and garments with slight flaws may be found in the shop at greatly discounted prices as the company is careful to safeguard its reputation for high quality. Hosiery, socks and accessories are also stocked, both here and at their other, smaller factory shop near Doncaster.

Well worth the journey!

JOHN SMEDLEY

Factory Shop
Lea Mills Lea Bridge
Matlock Derbyshire
DE4 5AG
Tel: 01629 534571

Men's and ladies' fine gauge, luxury knitwear, seconds & perfects

Open
Mon - Sun
10.00am - 4.00pm

also at
John Smedley Ltd
Rands Lane
Armthorpe
Doncaster DN3 3DY
Tel: 01302 832346

Open
Mon - Sat
10.00am - 3.30pm
Closed Bank Holidays and factory holidays
(telephone for details)

Large free car park

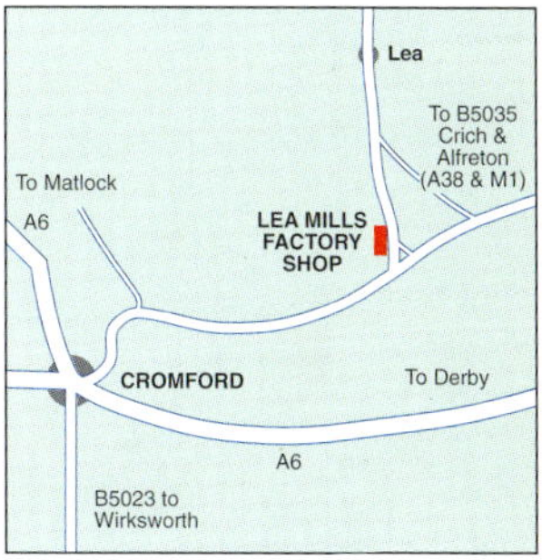

DE BRADELEI
—MILL SHOP—

De Bradelei House
Chapel Street
Belper
Derbyshire DE56 1AR
Tel: 01773 829830
Fax: 01773 829822

Stylish discount
ladieswear, menswear,
rugged outdoor wear
& shoes
Soft furnishings & giftware

Opening hours:
7 days a week
Mon – Fri 9.30am – 5.30pm
Sat 9.30am – 6.00pm
Sun & Bank Holidays
11.00am – 5.00pm

Free car parking at the rear of the building.
Access, toilets and parking for the disabled.

Chevin Coffee Shop
Serving delicious
home-cooked food

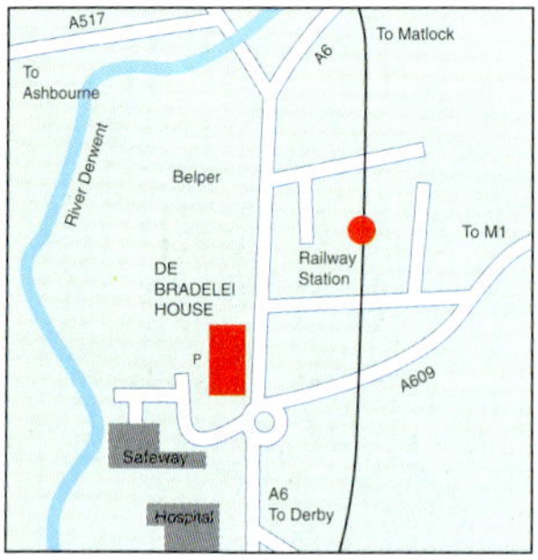

DE BRADELEI MILL SHOP

This family owned business is housed in a totally refurbished old hosiery mill with a fascinating history. Silk hose for George III and silk stockings worn by Queen Victoria at her Coronation were manufactured here, as was the vest worn by Admiral Lord Nelson at Trafalgar. After many years as a disused shell it is fitting that once again high quality clothing can be obtained here. You will recognise many famous brands for sale in the attractive shops ranged around a pretty courtyard.

The company specialises in High Street and Designer labels with up to 70% discount, achieved by the company acting as a clearing house to clear their end of line or surplus stock. All the stock is well displayed. Friendly, efficient and knowledgeable staff are on hand to help you. In fact, everything you would expect from any other high quality shop - the big difference is the lower prices. Womenswear includes Windmoor, Précis Petite, Planet, Four Seasons, Jaeger Knitwear, Phase Eight, French Connection, Gerard Pasquier, Joyce Ridings, Liz Claiborne, Country Casuals, Elvi, Elle and others.

A large Menswear Department has an excellent selection of both casual and formal wear from Wolsey, French Connection, Great Plains, Ben Sherman, Haggar, Lambretta and International Designer labels from Robert Leonard's Menswear. The Shoe Department also stocks many famous brands.

The new Giftware Department has Liberty, Butlers Grove Foods, White Porcelain Tableware, table linen, candles and photo frames. The Ponden Mill Shop supplies household linens, bedding and curtains.

END OF THE LINE FURNITURE

On your way north up the busy A6 through Ambergate you have probably passed this little shop. **End of the Line Furniture** is a *little* shop full of *big* surprises—top quality upholstered furniture at 40-50% below the normal retail price.

All the furniture has hardwood frames properly constructed to last a life time. Springing is also constructed for lasting comfort and endurance. As the proprietor says "You can tell the quality by the *weight* of the piece." There is a good selection of styles in two and three seater sofas and chairs, some based on old traditional designs with feather-filled seat cushions, others more contemporary and covered in the most luxurious fabrics. If what you want is not in stock, you can choose any style to be made up in any of the wide range of fabrics available. You may like some of the brilliantly coloured chenilles, faded regency stripes or pale coloured cotton damasks—the choice is yours. Whatever you choose will be made especially for you, and you can also choose your method of payment and know that you are buying extremely good quality at a very reasonable price.

Delivery can be arranged to anywhere in the UK or abroad—Athens being the furthest to date!

END OF THE LINE
FURNITURE
FACTORY
SHOP

32 Derby Road
Ambergate
Derbyshire DE56 2GE
Tel/Fax: 01773 856082

High quality upholstered furniture at discount prices

Open
Thur, Fri, Sat
10.00am - 5.00pm
Sun
1.00pm - 5.00pm
other times please telephone

On site parking
or nearby kerbside

also
420 Alfreton Road
Nottingham NG7 5NG

Tues, Wed, Fri, Sat, Sun

Telephone 0115 979 1002

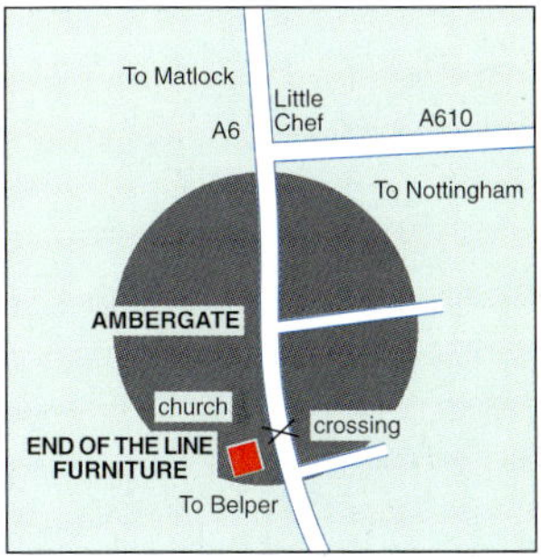

HADDON HALL

Haddon Hall
Bakewell
Derbyshire DE45 1LA
Tel: 01629 812855

Historic House with award-winning Gardens, Restaurant & Gift Shop Minton China mugs, prints, greetings cards, Belgian chocolates, gifts, preserves, leather goods, children's items

Open
1 April – 30 Sept 7 days
10.30am – 5.00pm
October Mon - Thur
10.30am - 4.30pm

Admission charge
Adult £5.75
Concessions £4.75

Gatehouse Gift Shop
FREE admission
Car Park 50p

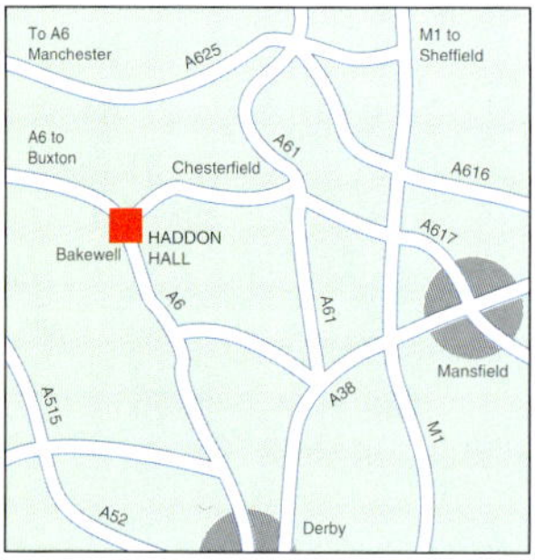

Haddon Hall

If you had to choose a most ancient but most romantic and intimate great house in all England, **Haddon Hall** would be high on your list - no wonder it has been the location for so many films and television series. And what glorious terraced gardens of roses, clematis and delphiniums surround the ancient honey coloured walls. Few visitors cannot but wonder at the warm splendour of the rafted timbers and mellow panelling of the great hall. Set in the Derbyshire Peak District, Haddon Hall is indeed a gem among England's country houses.

The Gatehouse Gift Shop will provide you with a memento of your visit, but it offers more than that. Indeed the range of products offered is really quite wide. There are Belgian chocolates and pots of preserves under the Haddon label, very good quality Minton China mugs with the Haddon design, prints and greeting cards, small leather goods and children's items - all high quality products at reasonable prices. The licensed restaurant, situated in the 17th century stable block, serves a variety of hot and cold lunches, morning coffee and cream teas. Definitely for those who prefer home-made food! All in all, a shopping trip to Haddon Hall is a delight.

Entrance to the shop is free, and there is ample car parking, but you will find it hard to resist sampling the delights of this beautiful manor house and its gardens, built on varying levels to make the most of its elevated site.

CAUDWELL'S MILL

Richard Martin

Caudwell's Mill is the only complete Victorian water-powered *roller* mill in the country that you can visit. The present mill was built in 1874 by John Caudwell and run by the family for over a century. It is now preserved by an educational charity. There are four floors of fascinating original machinery to explore, all driven from the turbines by belts and shafts, exhibitions to see and 'hands-on' models to try. It is well worth a visit. Pre-booked parties are guided by expert staff who can interpret the mill's history and technology.

The Mill Shop specialises in a range of quality flours to delight the discerning housewife. There are strong white and wholemeal flours for great bread and cakes, Malted Flake flour with a delightful aroma, and specialist pizza, French stick and pastry flours, all at competitive prices. There are álso soft self-raising and rye flours, oatmeal and a great range of 'Farmhouse' biscuits.

Around the Stable Yard are several working craftspeople, a craft shop and café. One old stable houses **The Mill Forge**, presided over by Bob Brown, blacksmith and creative artist. Many of the time-honoured methods of the traditional blacksmith are still used here to conjure up 'modern antiques' which somehow only a forge can produce. Whether it is a weather-vane, a Derby Ram fire-tool set, a chestnut roaster, a pair of reproduction hinges, window or door latches or simply that special 'thingamajig', Bob can certainly oblige with distinction.

Caudwell's Mill
Rowsley Matlock
Derbyshire DE4 2EB
Tel/Fax: 01629 734374

Freshly milled high quality wholemeal, white and speciality flours
Exhibition & guided tours available

Open 1 April to 31 October
Daily 11am – 6pm
1 November to 31 March
10am – 4.30pm,
but Jan & Feb weekends only

The Mill Forge
Tel: 01629 732220

Weather vanes, fire tools and commissions, reproduction hinges, catches and latches

Open as above

Large free car park approached from School Lane

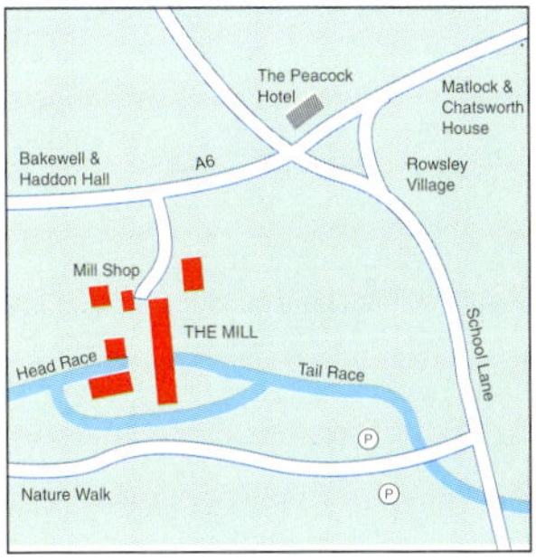

JAQUEST
Food Specialist

Spectrum House
21 Station Road
Bolsover Nr Chesterfield
Derbyshire S44 6BD
Tel/Fax: 01246 827972

Own smoked hams, bacon, fish and meats, cheeses, wines, preserves, delicatessen and much more

Open
Mon - Fri
9.00am - 6.00pm
Sat
9.00am - 1.00 pm

Farjals Country Foods
Mail Order
telephone for details and price list.
Wholesale and trade enquiries welcome.

Free roadside parking

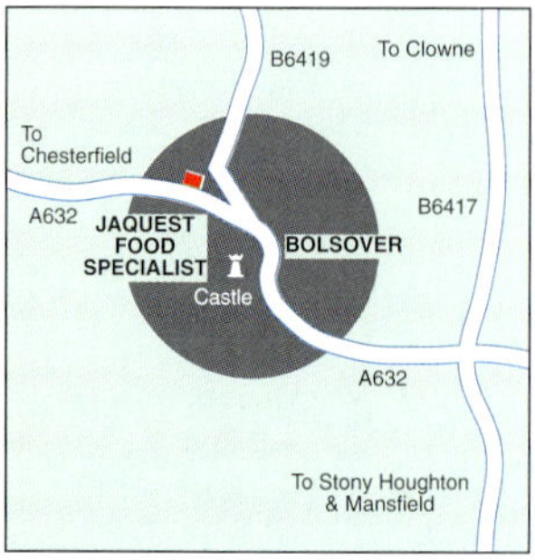

JAQUEST FOOD SPECIALIST

John Jaquest and his family have been in the fine food business for many years as producers, caterers, retailers and wholesalers and reckon to sell the finest available, whether produced by themselves or others. Such is their reputation that a growing number of people from all over the country will make a detour to visit this very special shop in the historic town of Bolsover.

Always keen to experiment in the smoke house with different products and flavours, when asked what he was doing, John had a habit of saying "*Oh, Farjalling!*" and so the arm of their business which sells their own smoked products direct became known as **Farjals Country Foods**. This range consists of the finest Scottish salmon, cured and smoked in a variety of ways, and other smoked fish. Also a most delectable range of smoked hams, smoked bacon, smoked chicken, duck, pork and other specialities. Let us not forget the air-dried hams, to be eaten wafer thin like Parma ham. Quality and service with a smile!

A visit to the shop is a treat in itself - very well stocked with all the things you normally have difficulty in finding, specialist sauces, preserves, pastas, nibbles and delicacies, plus dried fruit and nuts, and a fantastic range of chocolates. Hampers of all sizes can be made up - or choose your basket and fill it yourself. It will be gift-wrapped free of charge.

RIDGEWAY CRAFT CENTRE

Ridgeway Craft Centre is a lovingly restored 17th century collection of redundant farm buildings set around a courtyard in the rural heart of the Moss Valley. The attractive village of Ridgeway is easily accessible from the major routes in the area.

Traditional and modern crafts are brought together in the workshops and studios of the Craft Centre. **Silver and Gold Jewellery** is produced using precious and semi precious gem stones - from diamonds to the more unusual such as tsavorite (green garnet) and **It's About Time** repairs and restores antique clocks in addition to a selection for sale. **The Model Shack** is a dream come true for modelling enthusiasts of everything from radio controlled aircraft to boats, cars and rockets, and a wide range of kits and accessories. Handcrafted stoneware pottery, some painted and decorated with gold, is available from **Paul Mossman Pottery** who also makes *guaranteed* frost-proof large garden planters. Leather goods, including belts and handbags come from **Rodney Birdsall, Saddler and Leatherworker** and **Busy Bee** has a wide range of pictures and decoupage alongside an expert framing service. **Tiffany Land Stained Glass**, **Personally Yours** hand made chocolates and **Colonial Reproduction Furniture** complete the crafts on offer. Opening times may vary, please telephone to check if travelling a long way.

The Country Kitchen, which is licensed, serves delicious home-made, hot and cold food in the old farmhouse kitchen or outside, weather permitting!

RIDGEWAY
Craft Centre

Main Road Ridgeway
Derbyshire S12 3XR
General enquiries Mon-Fri
Tel. 01246 231111 ext 2449

Wide range of crafts
- traditional and modern
- workshops and studios

Open Tues - Sun
& Bank Holiday Mon
10.30am - 5.00pm

The Country Kitchen
tel. 0114 2473739

Silver & Gold Jewellery
tel. 0114 2477028

It's About Time
tel. 0114 2473196

The Model Shack
tel. 0114 2511761

Paul Mossman Pottery
tel. 0114 2511058

Rodney Birdsall
tel. 01246 230286

Busy Bee
tel. 0114 2513164

Tiffany Glass
tel. 0114 2477104

Personally Yours
tel. 0114 2478626

Colonial Reproduction Furniture
tel. 0114 2555009

Free car park

DENBY POTTERY VISITOR CENTRE

THE DENBY POTTERY COMPANY LTD 1809

Derby Road (B6179) Denby
Derbyshire DE5 8NX
Tel: 01773 740799

Visitor Centre
Opening times
Mon – Sat: 9.30am – 5.00pm
Sun: 10.00am – 5.00pm

Denby Factory Shop
(Perfects & Seconds)

The Cookery Emporium Shop
(Free demonstrations daily)

Dartington Crystal Factory Shop

Denby Handpainted
Decorative Ware

Shipley Garden Shop

Guided Factory Tours
(Small charge)

The Courtyard Restaurant

Picnic and Childrens Play Area

Ample free car park

Denby Factory Shops also at:

Broadmarsh Shopping Centre
Nottingham Tel: 0115 948 3932

Cheshire Oaks Designer Outlet
Village, Ellesmere Port
Tel: 0151 356 4943

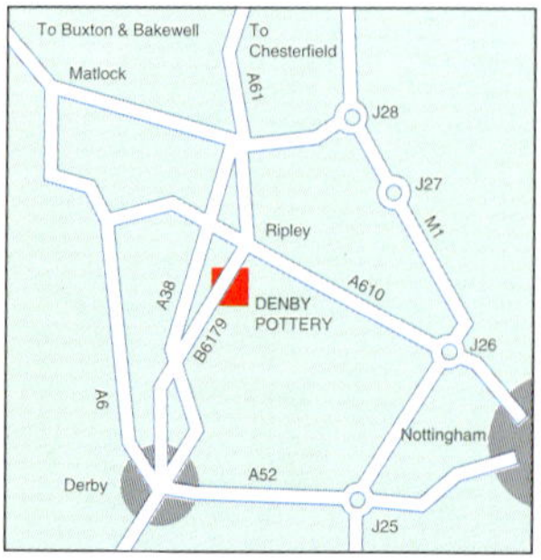

Most of us are familiar with the distinctive colours and designs of Denby Pottery, but did you know it is produced in the heart of rural Derbyshire? Nearly 200 years ago a fine seam of stoneware clay was discovered during road building and this became the basis for the origin of the production of this internationally renowned pottery.

Denby Pottery, although contemporary in design, fits happily in to any setting and is extremely practical – some of the designs of only thirty or forty years ago are now collectors items, as unlike more traditional patterns, styles and colours are changed to keep ahead of the trend – or should I say, to create the trend? All designs have a timeless elegance. You will find a good selection of second quality products (with only tiny flaws), and helpful, friendly staff. If you want to see how Denby is made, you will find a guided factory tour fascinating - learn how 30 pairs of hands touch a teacup on its journey from raw clay to finished piece. There is also an opportunity to "have a go" at painting a plate or making a frog.

The Cookery Emporium includes a state of the art cookshop and a full-scale cookery theatre where Denby's own chefs and guest celebrity chefs demonstrate their culinary skills. High quality cookware, kitchen gadgets and equipment from all over the world, including exclusive products from the U.S.A. are available. The demonstrations give you an opportunity to see them in action and give inspiration for new cooking and entertaining ideas. Allow plenty of time for your visit as the restaurant is extremely good also.

DAVID NIEPER

David Nieper is a long established family firm based in Derbyshire on the edge of the Peak District. They have their own factory shop and boutique nestled in the very heart of the factory, selling ladies lingerie and designer wear at genuine factory shop prices.

Situated on the edge of Alfreton's town centre, just off the A38 and junction 28 of the M1, there is a large, free car park and, for those needing refreshment, tea and coffee is available from the staff canteen.

Excellence in every detail is David Nieper's passion, every fabric individually selected and each design approved by David personally. Expert cutters and seamstresses ensure each garment is made to the highest possible standard, each one carefully examined.

Everyone shares in his enthusiasm for the beautiful garments made here, not least the ladies who work in the shop, who provide a warm welcome and are ready to offer advice if needed. They have a fine selection of one-off designer samples, exquisite lingerie, fabulous nightwear, blouses, skirts, holidaywear, dressing gowns and a wide selection of exclusive fabrics, laces and ribbons. Comfortable, spacious, air-conditioned changing rooms makes trying on easy. A free bra fitting service is also available from the highly trained staff.

The David Nieper Factory Shop and Boutique is simply not to be missed during your visit to the beautiful Peak District. Pop along to see them, take this advertisement and enjoy 10% off your purchases.

There is a mail order service too, so if you would like to receive a catalogue please call 01773 836000 and a copy will be sent to you.

David Nieper

FACTORY SHOP & BOUTIQUE

Nottingham Road
Alfreton
Derbyshire
DE55 7LE
Tel: 01773 833335 ext 218

Lingerie, housegowns, leisurewear, swimwear, cruisewear, separates

Open
Mon - Sat
9.00am - 5.00pm
including all Bank Holidays
except Christmas
and New Year

also Mail Order
tel: 01773 836000

Large free car park

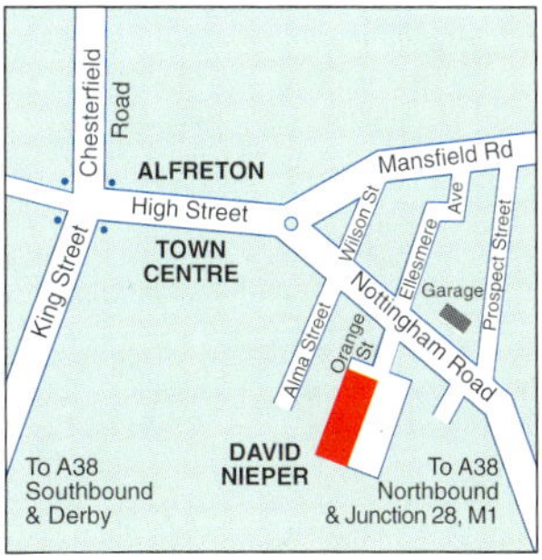

TUTBURY CRYSTAL

Tutbury

Tutbury Crystal Glass Ltd
Burton Street Tutbury
Staffordshire DE13 9NG
Tel: 01283 813281
Fax: 01283 813228

Handmade English Full Lead crystal (perfects and seconds)

Tea room

Open
Mon – Sat 9.00am – 5.00pm
Sun 11.00am – 4.00pm
Factory Tours by appointment
small charge min 12 persons

also at
Melbourne Crystal
& Gift Shop
4 Russell Yard
Melbourne Derbyshire
Tel: 01332 863811

Handmade English Full Lead crystal (perfects and seconds)

Open
Mon – Sat
9.00am – 5.00pm Sundays
Summer Season, December
Telephone for details

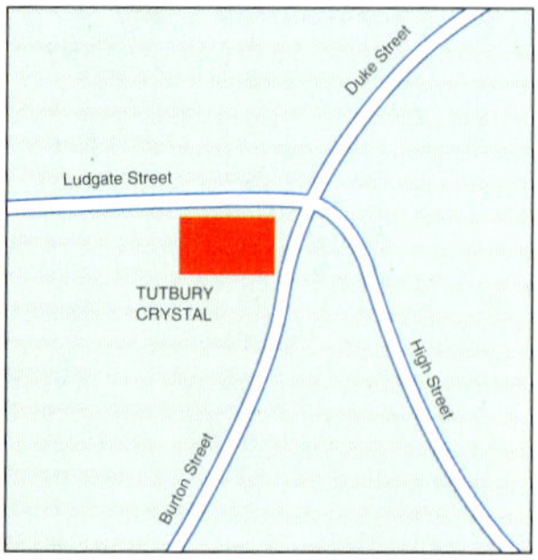

Tutbury is a small and ancient town, often missed as you travel the A50, but well worth a visit for its old buildings and its castle, in which Mary, Queen of Scots was imprisoned in 1569, before meeting her fateful end at Fotheringhay.

However, the prime purpose of your trip should be to visit **Tutbury Crystal**. The old glass factory has a long and chequered history, and produces most beautiful handmade, hand cut crystal, which has found its way into millions of homes across the World. Glass has been produced more or less continuously on this site since 1720. The skills involved in making such superb glass have been handed down through local families for centuries. You only need to examine any piece of Tutbury Crystal; feel its weight, notice the purity of the glass, the clarity and sparkle and the depth of cut to realise why it is so special.

The company produces a full range of giftware, vases, tableware and a few surprises at prices to suit all pockets. An engraving service is also available. There is always a good selection of seconds at very reasonable prices. They also stock ceramics, home accessories, textiles and toys. Why not finish your visit by booking a factory tour for a group of friends?

THE CURBOROUGH COLLECTION

A few miles from Lichfield, this working family farm has its old buildings converted to house a large collection of interesting articles for sale.

Antiques and Collectables cover the whole range of furniture, glass, china, pictures, books and sundry small items. Traditional kitchens, bedrooms and bathrooms can be supplied from an adjacent barn which also has AGA displays and demonstrations, plus the fireplace centre with fire surrounds for any style of home. The picture gallery displaying work by local artists is always popular, as is the **Farmshop** specialising in fresh produce, free range eggs and poultry.

The Arches, another large barn, is a constant delight to those looking for unusual and reasonably priced home accessories and handicraft supplies. There are wonderfully natural looking *wooden* flowers, interesting items made from flotsam, jetsam and shells, hand made dolls, teddy bears and dolls house items. You can also choose fabulous fabrics by well-known names for your own curtains and soft furnishings. The range of curtain poles is particularly good, and commemorative plaques and house names can be handcrafted.

On your way to **Mabels Restaurant and Tearoom** look into the glass-blowing studio. Before you leave the farm, order hanging baskets, tubs for your patio, or buy plants and enquire about having your garden redesigned.

Curborough Hall Farm truly has something for everyone.

Antique and Craft Centre
Curborough Hall Farm
Watery Lane Curborough
Lichfield Staffs WS13 8ES
Tel: 01543 262595

Antiques & collectables
(Open Tues - Sun 10.30 am - 5.00 pm)
Traditional kitchens, bedrooms & bathrooms
AGA display centre
Fireplace centre
Curtains & soft furnishings
Curtain poles
Picture gallery
Hand made decorative glass, wooden flowers & home accessories
Hand made dolls, teddy bears & dolls house items
Rubber Art Stamps & cards
Ceramic supplies & workshop
Handcrafted house names, plaques & memorials
Hanging baskets & tubs
Plant nursery & garden design
(Open Mon - Sat 9.00 am - 5.00 pm Sun 10.00 am - 5.00 pm)
Farmshop (open 7 days 10.00 am - 5.00 pm)
Mabels Restaurant & Tearoom
(open Tues - Sun 10.30 am - 5.00 pm)

Unless stated otherwise units are open: Wed - Sun and B.H. Mon
10.30 am - 5.00 pm
Large free car park

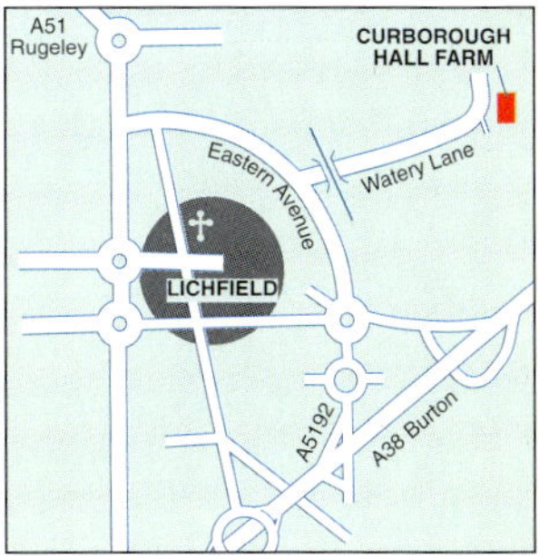

Cannock Beds

Martindale
Hawks Green Cannock
Staffs WS11 2XT
Tel: 01543 438200
Fax: 01543 506237
Email:
sales@cannockbeds.co.uk
www.cannockbeds.co.uk

*Wrought iron beds,
headboards, bedlinen
& accessories*

Shop open:
Mon - Sat 9.00 am - 5.00 pm
Sun 10.00 am - 4.00 pm
Mail order catalogue request/order line open:
Mon - Fri 8.00 am - 8.00 pm
Sat 9.00 am - 5.00 pm
Sun 10.00 am - 4.00 pm

Cannock Gates™

*Solid timber &
wrought iron gates
By mail order or shop*

The Garden Factory™

*Garden furniture, rose arches,
arbours, gazebos
By mail order or shop*
Tel: 01543 462500
Fax: 01543 506237

Shop hours as Cannock Beds

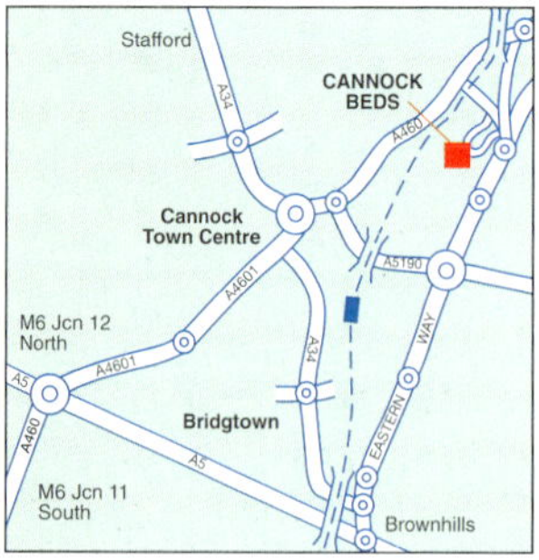

Cannock Beds

Many of you will be familiar with **Cannock Gates** as manufacturers and direct suppliers of high quality, solid wrought iron and timber gates. Established in 1983, they have an extensive range of gates and railings available through their mail order catalogue. **The Garden Factory** - part of the same company - offers a wide selection of products such as garden and patio furniture, rose arches, arbours, trellis and gazebos. You can find products from both ranges at the **Factory Shop** on the outskirts of Cannock, seven days a week.

Cannock Beds is part of the same company and the product range is also available at the Factory Shop. Contemporary and traditional designs are available as single, double and king-size with a choice of finishes and finials, most can also be made as four-posters. Each one is hand-crafted to the highest standards, but sold at a very reasonable price with a lifetime guarantee against faulty workmanship or materials. High quality mattresses, pillows, duvets and beautiful bedlinen can be purchased at the same time, either at the shop or through the mail order catalogue. Separate headboards in all sizes and designs can be supplied to fit your existing divan. A wide range of bedside tables, chairs, curtain poles and storage units ensure you can have the bedroom of your dreams!

TAMWORTH CASTLE

Tamworth, as you pass the signs off the busy A5/M42 junction, may at first glance seem an unlikely place to find a magnificent castle with 800 years of history. **Tamworth Castle**, perched above the water meadows and the Castle Pleasure Grounds, but in the town centre, has a curtain wall and shell-keep dating from the 12th century, with apartments added in practically every century since.

Your journey of discovery starts in the courtyard where Tudor and Jacobean buildings nestle within the medieval fortress walls. Inside delightful period rooms give a glimpse into the life and times of past owners and occupants. Pause in the Tower bedroom and see the Black Lady ghost! The castle is famous for its *living images* (hi-tec talking figures). Baron Marmion welcomes you in the Norman Exhibition, where you can find out about medieval castles, and a 19th century prisoner talks through his cell door in the Tamworth Story, which traces the town's history from Roman times. Many interesting hands on features, a quiz and a slide show, make this a fun and fascinating visit for all ages.

The Shop has a good selection of historical souvenir items, plus guidebooks, local history and children's activity guides. Admission to the shop is free, ask at the entrance, but it is a strong mind that can resist the temptation to explore. The Great Hall is available for corporate functions.

The Great Little English Castle
TAMWORTH CASTLE

The Holloway
Tamworth
Staffordshire B79 7LR
Tel: 01827 709626
Fax: 01827 709630

Castle Museum

Shop - historical, gift & souvenir items

Open daily:
Mon - Sat 10.00 am - 5.30 pm
Sun 2.00 pm - 5.30 pm
Last entry 4.30 pm
Please check times between 1 Nov & mid Feb

Admission to the Shop is FREE, ask at the reception.

Castle admission charge.

Unfortunately limited access for wheelchairs because of the steep entrance path and many stairs inside. Please telephone for full details.

Car parking well signed off A51 Riverdrive

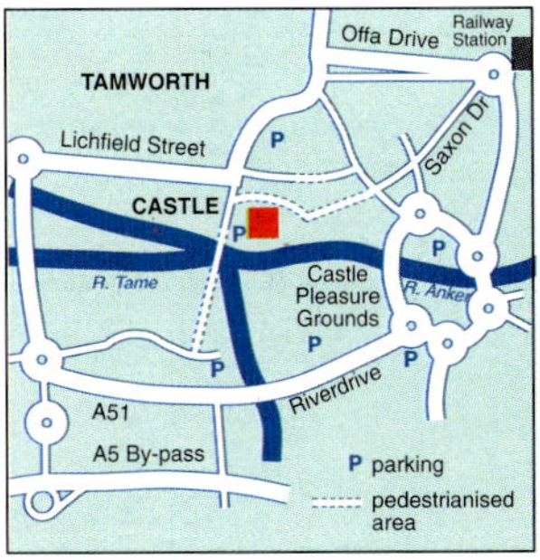

INDEX

LOCATION AND PRODUCTS

Further copies of this book or others in the series may be obtained from bookshops or direct from the publishers.

The Alternative Shopping Guide
Derbyshire, Staffordshire, Cheshire & North Shropshire
ISBN 1-902634-00-4 (2nd Edition) price £3.95 (plus 50p p&p)

The Alternative Shopping Guide
Central South & South West England
ISBN 0-9523761-8-0 (2nd Edition) price £3.50 (plus 50p p&p)

The Alternative Shopping Guide
East of England
ISBN 0-9523761-9-9 (3rd Edition) price £3.50 (plus 50p p&p)

The Alternative Shopping Guide
Heart of England
ISBN 0-9523761-7-2 price £3.50 (plus 50p p&p)

The Alternative Shopping Guide
Lancashire & Lake District, North West England
ISBN 0-9523761-4-8 price £3.50 (plus 50p p&p)

The Alternative Shopping Guide
South East England
ISBN 0-9523761-3-X (2nd Edition) price £3.50 (plus 50p p&p)

Please make your cheque payable to The Stable Publishing Company (no order will be accepted without prior payment) and post to:

The Stable Publishing Company
Woolsthorpe by Belvoir
Grantham
Lincolnshire
NG32 1NT

Tel: 01476 870770
Fax: 01476 870887
www.wctb.co.uk/magazine/alternat.htm

Books in the series due out shortly:

The Alternative Shopping Guide
South West Scotland

The Alternative Shopping Guide
Wales

The Alternative Shopping Guide
Yorkshire & Northumbria

This page has been left blank for your own notes.